Jaymee

The Story of Child B

SARAH BARCLAY

VIKING

VIKING

Published by the Penguin Group

Penguin Books Ltd, 27 Wrights Lane, London w8 5tz, England

Penguin Books USA Inc., 375 Hudson Street, New York, New York 10014, USA

Penguin Books Australia Ltd, Ringwood, Victoria, Australia

Penguin Books Canada Ltd, 10 Alcorn Avenue, Toronto, Ontario, Canada m4v 3b2

Penguin Books (NZ) Ltd, 182–190 Wairau Road, Auckland 10, New Zealand

Penguin Books Ltd, Registered Offices: Harmondsworth, Middlesex, England

First published 1996

1 3 5 7 9 10 8 6 4 2

First edition

Set in 11/14 pt Monotype Sabon
Typeset by Datix International Limited, Bungay, Suffolk
Printed in England by Clays Ltd, St Ives plc

A CIP catalogue record for this book is available from the British Library

ISBN 0–670–87050–1

For Richard and Rebecca

and for Jaymee and my late father, Michael Barclay,
both of whom taught me the meaning of courage

Contents

Acknowledgements

I am indebted to Steve Hewlett, the editor of *Panorama*, firstly for allowing me to spend six months making 'The Story of Child B', a programme which he knew might never be broadcast because of the legal restrictions in place at the time, and, secondly, for granting me leave of absence from the BBC to write this book. To Mike Robinson, the *Panorama* producer with whom I made the film, I owe particular thanks, not only for his exceptionally high journalistic standards and professional judgement, but also for a valuable friendship and shared vision of the projects on which we have worked together.

Many people have given up their time to provide me with help and information during the course of writing the book, so all errors and omissions are most definitely my own. My first thanks must go to Dr Peter Gravett, who has answered my endless lists of questions with great patience as well as kindly agreeing to check the manuscript for medical accuracy. Dr Simon Meller from the Royal Marsden Hospital gave me invaluable insight into the point at which a doctor decides that cure is no longer an option, Professor Grant Prentice at the Royal Free Hospital provided me with statistics on bone marrow transplantation and donor lymphocyte infusion, and Professor John Goldman at the Hammersmith Hospital explained how those who treat adults and those who treat children may sometimes disagree. Thanks, too, must go to

ACKNOWLEDGEMENTS

Stephen Thornton, the chief executive of the Cambridge and Huntingdon Health Commission for putting his professional neck on the line by explaining why he refused to pay the bill for Jaymee's treatment and for taking the ensuing criticism on the chin. Had it not been for the encouragement of Derek Johns at A. P. Watt and Clare Alexander and Anya Waddington at Viking, the book would probably have remained no more than an idea, and it certainly could not have been written without the cooperation of the Bowen family. To them I owe special thanks. But my most important debt of gratitude is to my husband, Richard, for his constant support and belief in me, which make it all worthwhile.

Introduction

I met Jaymee Bowen for the first time on 10 April 1995. For me and for Mike Robinson, the *Panorama* producer with whom I was to spend the next six months making a film about her progress, the meeting was the culmination of several weeks of trying to make contact with the elusive ten-year-old girl known only as Child B. Before that first meeting we had managed to create a stereotyped image of what she would be like, a sort of composite picture of a sweet, sick child whose plight would capture the nation's hearts. For Jaymee wasn't the first and certainly won't be the last child whose parents refuse to accept a diagnosis of terminal illness and decide to set out on a desperate search for a cure.

But from the moment we met her, we realized that this was no stereotype. Jaymee's story certainly captured the nation's hearts when it was eventually told, but this is because she is very much her own person, not a girl prepared to conform to other people's images of a child with a life-threatening illness. She is a bright, intelligent individual with an extraordinary lack of self-pity and an uncompromising logic and insight which give her a maturity well beyond her years.

We wanted to make a film about her because her story seemed to raise so many complex issues about the National Health Service at the end of the twentieth century. For us, Jaymee's case highlighted a moment of cultural change in the NHS and revealed some of the medical and financial decision-making which, until recently, has taken place behind the proverbial closed doors. Her story also raised questions about the risks, rewards and ethics of experimental medicine.

When do doctors decide that there is no reasonable chance of a cure? How do they make that decision and how can we be sure they are right? Should we expect the NHS to pay the bill for experimental treatment if the chance of survival is slim? How long should a parent go on fighting to save a precious child?

Jaymee's story asks all these questions but, above all, her story is a human one. The choice facing the Bowen family when they were told that she had no more than two months to live was a choice which any of us might find ourselves facing if we were told that we or our children were suffering from a terminal illness. That there are a personality and a voice as strong as hers at the heart of it makes Jaymee's story even more compelling. It helps us to understand just what is at stake when illness threatens to overcome us, and that at such agonizing moments there are no easy answers.

1

An Extraordinary Girl

When leukaemia selected Jaymee Bowen as a target, it chose a formidable opponent. She was only six, but even before her illness had acquired a strength of character that seemed to mark her out as someone whose life would be remarkable: she was intelligent, articulate and self-assured, and everyone who knew her said that behind the childlike exterior Jaymee Bowen had a mind of her own. Just like her father. When David Bowen describes his first and, in many ways, most precious, child, it could just as well be a self-portrait.

'You get your fingers burned with Jaymee if you upset her,' David said. 'Jaymee has a very analytical sort of mind, very inquiring, very probing. If anyone talks down to her from on high and delivers a sermon, that's water off a duck's back to her. You have to show her and explain to her and give her the facts and she will make up her own mind. She won't allow anybody to make it up for her.'

Jaymee looks like her father too. She has the same dark skin, brown curly hair and large brown eyes – serious eyes which scrutinize and evaluate and light up only on rare occasions and never to order. 'People have to earn our trust and our respect,' David said. 'It isn't something that's granted to them by virtue of their position or their age or their job.'

David regards Jaymee, the eldest of his five children, as the flagbearer for the next generation of the extensive Bowen family.

David Bowen was five years old when his parents, Ossie and Rita, left Georgetown, Guyana and came to live in England. It was 1968, two years after the former British colony had been granted independence. David's brother, Graham, was three and his sister, Debbie, just one year old. Even though all three children are grown up now and have children of their own, Rita provides the emotional thread that keeps the Bowen family together.

Today, the small semi-detached house in a long, straight South London street where she and her husband, Ossie, have lived for fifteen years remains home to whichever of their children or grandchildren needs looking after at whatever time, day or night. It is full of beds and children's belongings and there are photographs of the family everywhere. Although Rita has a full-time job, as a secretary at Croydon Council, her family always comes first. She and Ossie were married when they were both eighteen. They are fifty now and remain a strikingly handsome couple who are still entirely committed to their children.

Rita Bowen is part Asian by descent. Her mother was Portuguese and her father, whom she hardly knew, was Indian. David's father, Ossie, is Afro-Caribbean. David describes him as 'my back-up, my co-pilot, my stunt-double', with whom he discusses everything and to whom he turns for support. Without that support, David would be the first to admit, his struggle for Jaymee would have been much more difficult. His parents knew how to overcome obstacles.

In Georgetown, Rita worked as a secretary for a large industrial company. Ossie had been in the police force, working as a motor mechanic, but then left for a much better-paid job in the mines, maintaining all the heavy equipment. After Independence, Ossie and Rita, both aged twenty-three, decided it was time to make a new start, particularly as they both had family in England. They'd been told life would be better in Britain. Instead, they had a harsh awakening. 'In Georgetown everybody had a servant,' Rita said. 'I just took it for granted. In the morning, all I had to do was to get myself up and ready for work and the nanny would look after the children.' But in England, she had to fend for herself. Rita arived in the summer, so that David would be ready to start school in the autumn. Ossie followed five months later.

Rita and Ossie had brought almost nothing with them because they'd been told they could get 'everything' in England. But it wasn't as simple as it had seemed from a distance. Before Ossie's arrival, Rita found herself sharing one rented room in a house in Balham with the three children. She hated it and wanted to go home. When he arrived and they started looking for a flat, they came face to face with racial prejudice for the first time.

'I would see a room advertised,' Rita told me. 'We'd ring up and they'd say come round, and we'd go round straight away and they would take one look at us and say sorry the room's taken.'

Ossie is harsher: 'Racism has made us fight and fight and fight all the time to achieve what we want.' Certainly they both succeeded in getting jobs – Rita as a secretary at the local college, Ossie as a mechanic for London Transport. They say they tried not to imbue their children with a sense of racial prejudice, but David is convinced that part of his own determination to succeed came from a sense that somehow he was inferior. 'There were quite a few instances where people used to look down on me from on high and I was just sort of second best,' he said.

The eldest of the three children, David was, Rita says, always very bright but also introspective, a thinker. He was also extraordinarily neat and tidy, a boy who even folded his dirty clothes meticulously before they were washed. Today, David is still fastidious about his appearance, always smartly dressed, whatever the occasion.

He went to Selhurst School in Croydon, a former grammar school which retained the formality of school gowns and strict discipline. He got excellent O levels but left at sixteen on his mother's advice. She thought he would be better getting some vocational qualifications rather than staying on to do A levels. Both parents now say that had they known their way round the system, David might have ended up with a better education and then he would have been able to do 'anything he wanted'.

As a teenager, David was reserved and did not socialize easily. He didn't show much interest in girls or going to parties and preferred to keep himself to himself. He hasn't changed. 'I believe in keeping my emotions to myself,' he told me. 'It's a failing that I think I have, because partners have commented on the fact that the longer they're with me the less they know about me or what makes me tick because I never discuss things like that, I'm just very much within myself because I'm just a very calculating person. I think about things quite a lot and I don't believe in frivolous conversation.'

What David has always had, however, is a steely determination to succeed in whatever he does. His father remembers the conversation they had with a careers adviser just before David left school. 'He told him, "I want to be a pilot." The man said, "OK and what's your second choice?" "A pilot," David replied. "And what's your third choice?" "A pilot. I want to be a pilot," David insisted.' Forty-nine thousand nine hundred and ninety-nine other people had the same idea, there were just fifteen places on the training scheme, and David was several years younger than most of the other candidates. He reached the shortlist for the final thirty but wasn't accepted. It was his first real taste of failure.

'I was very disappointed, it was a real blow emotionally,' he said. 'It didn't knock me down, but it was something I didn't rationalize until many years later.'

He ended up doing a diploma in engineering and technology at the local college in Croydon. Then he decided it was time to do something which would earn him 'serious money'. Computers seemed to be the answer, so he went to a polytechnic in central London to do a degree in computer studies. Before he left, he'd already been offered a job. 'I have an unyielding desire to have nice things and I've always felt that my determination and drive to succeed were based around the fact that if you don't have enough money you can't have what you like. You have to settle for second best,' David said.

He started working as a systems analyst, trouble-shooting for companies whose computers went wrong. It meant being called out at any time of the day or night. It was a job which required enormous precision and logic and it was well paid. At the age of nineteen he began to get a taste of the kind of material wealth he'd been chasing. 'Making money is an addiction,' he told me. Later on, it began to cause him problems.

Halfway through his computer course, he met a girl called Alyson who lived near his parents. She was walking her dog in the park which overlooked Ossie and Rita's house and David began seeing her regularly. She was just fifteen and still at school. It was a relationship of which neither of his parents approved. They thought she and David weren't suited and that Alyson was not ambitious enough to be a partner for their son. But David was attracted by Alyson's 'bright, tomboyish personality', and by her looks. 'She was thin and pretty with large, greeny-blue eyes,' he said. Despite his parents' disapproval, the relationship continued. Alyson left school and joined a youth training scheme and on 31 March 1984, when she was eighteen, they got married in the local church, which Rita attended regularly and still does today. Alyson was three months pregnant. She moved out of her parents' house and into a flat with David. Even though they'd both been married at eighteen themselves, Rita and Ossie still felt that David and Alyson were too young.

Jaymee was born on 5 August in Mayday Hospital in Croydon. It was a normal birth and David was there, as he has been for all but one of his children's births. 'I remember sitting there looking at Jaymee thinking, she's hideous, because when babies are first born they're all grey and look as if they need ironing,' he said. But after a while he could see she was going to look like him. 'Jaymee has always had a special place in my heart because she was my first child and I think there's a different bond between you and your first-born child than there is with any other children.' She was a good baby, only crying when there was genuinely something to cry about, a character trait she retains to this day. In spite of all she has had to endure, Jaymee is not someone who indulges in self-pity. Like her father, she prefers to keep her emotions to herself.

Ossie and Rita had been right to be concerned about the relationship between David and Alyson. He was often called away from home at short notice to sort out a company's computer system, leaving Alyson to cope with Jaymee on her own. Inevitably they began to grow apart.

'There was enormous pressure,' David said. 'I was still very young and as a young parent away from home for such huge lengths of time, that can be pretty difficult to deal with.'

Nevertheless, eight months after Jaymee's birth, Alyson was pregnant again, though by now the relationship was almost over. Charlotte was born on 17 January 1986; this time, however, David wasn't there for the birth. He was in

Manchester on business but had left his mobile telephone number with Alyson's parents so that they could get in touch when she went into labour. He says they didn't contact him and only told him several hours later that he had another daughter. 'I got in my car, drove all the way down, did my stuff, then drove back up again,' he said. It meant his first encounter with Charlotte was a brief one. Two months later, David left Alyson and the girls. Jaymee was just eighteen months old.

With two young children, Alyson found it increasingly difficult to cope. When David and Alyson had been separated for a year and a half, he became convinced that Jaymee and Charlotte would be better off living with him.

There were precedents for this in the Bowen family too. David's father says he can't remember anyone in the family who has had children and left them to be looked after by 'the other half' after the relationship has failed, and that includes his own three children, all of whose marriages have ended in divorce.

But although Ossie and Rita knew that David's marriage was effectively over, they did not know what he was planning. 'He generally looks at things, sizes them up, thinks about them, comes to his conclusion, tells you nothing and acts on it,' Ossie said. And that was exactly what happened. In July 1987, having decided in his own mind that Jaymee and Charlotte should be with him rather than with Alyson, he went to the flat one night and simply took them away. Charlotte was eighteen months old and Jaymee almost three. Since that night, they have never lived with their mother again.

Rita said that although Jaymee, in particular, seemed happier when she was with David than with Alyson, she felt instinctively that children should remain with their mother and she was worried that David would not be able to cope either. Realizing that Alyson needed support, Rita offered to help look after the girls if Alyson's mother would share some of the work with her. Rita still had a full-time job and could not have taken full responsibility for two small children but, with some support, she thought she could manage. However, Alyson's mother refused, so the girls remained with their father and his new girlfriend, Debbie. David and Alyson were divorced in September 1988. The terms of the settlement said that Alyson should be given 'reasonable contact' with Jaymee and Charlotte. But because they were both so young when David took them away, neither has any real memories of her.

Rita says simply: 'There are always three sides to a story. Her side, his side and the truth, somewhere in the middle.'

When Alyson discovered that Jaymee was ill, she renewed attempts to see her daughters, anxious that if Jaymee was going to die, she at least had the right to know who her mother was.

Between the divorce in 1988 and 1993, David says Alyson had seen Jaymee and Charlotte just four times. As far as the children were concerned, David's new girlfriend, Debbie, who became his second wife, was the woman they called, and still call, Mummy. The night David took Jaymee and Charlotte away from Alyson, he brought them back to Debbie, who was heavily pregnant with their first child.

She was completely unprepared for the sudden arrival of two small girls whom she hardly knew. David hadn't discussed his plans with her, he simply turned up with Jaymee and Charlotte, but from the start Debbie assumed almost total responsibility for them. For the next four years, she was the woman who looked after them and brought them up and to whom they still remain extremely close. When Rita saw how well they were being cared for, she stopped being so concerned about their lack of contact with Alyson.

It was in December 1994 that Jaymee and Charlotte discovered that the woman they had been told was their 'Aunt'

Alyson was really their mother. David says he kept the truth from them because they had seen almost nothing of Alyson since they were babies. He thought it was better to tell them when they were old enough to understand, instead of wondering why their mother played no real part in their lives.

Jaymee says it made no real emotional difference to her because she had had so little contact with Alyson over the years. She is adamant that learning the truth about her real mother made little impact. As far as she is concerned, the person who had been, and remains, her mother was Debbie.

David had met Debbie, also a computer systems analyst, through work. He was still living with Alyson when their relationship began but, as far as he was concerned, that marriage had already broken down. David and Debbie were married in 1989. Their first son, James, had been born two years earlier, just a week after Jaymee and Charlotte had arrived to live with them. By now, the two girls had already experienced more upheaval in their short and unconventional lives than most children of their age. But they had also acquired a certain resilience, and they had got used to David being away working for much of the time and to Debbie being the person who looked after them.

But in December that same year, when Jaymee was five, a darker shadow appeared on the horizon, which none of them was prepared for and which overturned the fragile normality of the children's lives. For no apparent reason, Jaymee's left cheek began to swell until there was a lump the size of a golf ball. Her doctor diagnosed mumps. Over the next ten months, the lump vanished and reappeared five times and was, according to Jaymee, 'very painful'.

As time went on, it was obvious that it couldn't be mumps. The first three times the lump had appeared, Jaymee had been given antibiotics and within a week the swelling had disappeared. But when it reappeared for the fourth time, it was more difficult to treat and it didn't go away.

Debbie was beginning to get worried. David had gone to Singapore for three months on business, leaving her with the three children. It was an enormous responsibility and she was pregnant again, so while David was away she took the children with her to stay with her mother near Newmarket. It was when she was there that another GP suggested referring Jaymee to the local hospital for tests. She was given a CT scan to try and determine the cause of the lump. The consultant, suspecting that what Jaymee had was more serious than mumps, referred her to Addenbrooke's Hospital in Cambridge, the largest teaching hospital in the area.

Jaymee was admitted on 17 September 1990 and a battery of tests began. Under anaesthetic, a biopsy was performed – a slice was taken out of the tumour to be examined. Fluid was removed from her spine to see if there were any signs of rogue cells in her central nervous system, and a sample of bone marrow was tested. Another, more detailed scan was taken of her whole body, her blood tested and her liver function analysed. By now David was back, and both he and Debbie were there to hear the results when they came through three days later.

'I thought the tests were fairly routine at the time,' David said. 'But the air of anticipation was definitely there. You could see the doctors weren't happy about something. You could see it in their eyes. I remember getting called into a room and that's always a bad sign.' It was left to a young doctor to break the news to David. 'He said, "Your daughter's got cancer."'

Reflecting on that time, David says, with the benefit of hindsight, that this was the period in his life where his addiction to money had begun to get the better of him, to the point where it might easily have cost him his daughter's life. 'The more money you earn, the more addictive it becomes and the more difficult it becomes to control your family life. It is all-consuming,' he said. 'It was only because Debbie took Jaymee to the doctor for the first four times that it was picked up. That was my biggest jolt. I know that if Debbie hadn't been there, I would have missed it. I would not have taken Jaymee back to the doctor. I would have assumed it was mumps, carried on and Jaymee would have died. There would have been nothing I could have done about it. I could have been sitting there with a great deal of money but I would have lost my daughter.'

In the two years before Jaymee's cancer was diagnosed, David had set up a property business and was at last making the serious money of which he'd dreamed. Enough money to buy a large country house in Lincolnshire. Enough money, he said, 'to go out and buy a £90,000 car without blinking, just on a whim. Jaymee was cocooned in a world where she was protected and she was treated differently because she went to school in a brand-new Rolls-Royce every day. All the other kids didn't.'

But in April 1990, while the unexplained lump on Jaymee's cheek continued to vanish and reappear, David's company went into liquidation. The relatively short-lived days of serious money were over, and as a result of loans he had undertaken to guarantee himself, he was declared bankrupt.

'Jaymee had everything, everything that a little girl could possibly want. She wanted for absolutely nothing,' he said proudly. Except good health. Five years later, when he needed it most, money was the one thing David Bowen did not have at his disposal to help his daughter.

2

Some Cause for Hope

'You forget what it's like to be normal,' Jaymee said. 'For me, life before I was six was normal. Nothing after that was normal. That's a whole five years. A long time. The memory of being normal stays with you. I think you just forget how to do it.'

Jaymee became a medical celebrity from the moment her cancer was diagnosed. Her doctors had seen only one other case like it before. She had non-Hodgkin's lymphoma, a cancer which originates either in the lymph nodes (found in groups, mostly round the neck, armpits, groin and some major blood vessels in the chest and abdomen), which play an important part in the body's immune system, or in other organs like the liver, spleen, bowel or bone marrow. What was so unusual about Jaymee's case was that the tumour was in her cheek. There were no other signs of the disease anywhere else in her body.

But within that tumour there were traces of a second cancer, leukaemia. Leukaemia is a cancer of the blood, affecting the white blood cells which then reproduce wildly, destroying the normal constituents of blood.

Every second, the bone marrow, the spongy tissue inside the bones, produces about three million red blood cells, which carry oxygen to all the vital tissues of the body, and 120,000 white cells, which help the body fight infections. When leukaemic cells appear, they go to war on those healthy blood cells, multiplying and obliterating them and destroying the body's ability to fight infection. As the disease progresses, it becomes increasingly difficult for the bone marrow to produce any normal blood cells at all. Thirty years ago, there was little doctors could do to cure leukaemia and patients would gradually succumb to infection and die. Since then, complex cocktails of drugs – chemotherapy – have been developed which attack and destroy cancer cells, leading either to a complete cure or to periods of 'remission' when the cancer dies down.

When Jaymee's doctors broke the news, they tried to soften the blow for David and Debbie by telling them there was an 80–85 per cent chance of curing her. 'If the doctor hadn't cleverly linked the news that she had cancer with the fact that there was such a high chance of curing Jaymee, perhaps I would have been in more of a state,' David said. 'But he assured me it was a common cancer in children. Of course you aren't going to worry so much then if you're being told, "Your child has cancer but we can deal with this, don't worry." It gives you something to hold on to mentally.'

The question was what to tell Jaymee. How much could a six-year-old be expected to understand about an illness like this without being unnecessarily frightened? David and Debbie decided to tell her that she had something wrong with her blood. But they didn't use the words cancer or leukaemia. They just told her that she would have to spend some time in hospital and that she was going to get better.

'I don't think I was particularly bothered about it,' Jaymee said. 'All I knew was that I was going to have this medicine and it was going to make my face go down. That was it. I didn't know it was anything serious.'

It was to be a carefully masterminded campaign of destruction lasting two years, with the most intensive dose of chemotherapy being given in the first six months. The doctors hoped that most of the cancer cells would be destroyed by that first dose and that Jaymee would go into remission. Then the next stage of the treatment would begin, involving more drugs designed to ensure that if any cancer cells had remained behind undetected, they would be destroyed too. It was particularly important to get rid of any cells which might have found their way into Jaymee's central nervous system, where they could attack her brain or spine.

After that, the final dose of chemotherapy would, if successful, make sure the cancer didn't come back. Each dose of drugs would be given in special sequences so as to have the maximum effect on the cancer cells while doing the least possible damage to Jaymee's normal cells and body tissues. It would be a long haul but the doctors told David and Debbie she would be getting the best available treatment for her condition and the best possible chance of a cure.

There was, however, no time to lose. The treatment began the next day, and for the next three months, until Christmas Eve, Jaymee spent almost all her time in the children's cancer unit of Addenbrooke's Hospital. She remembers: 'I was told the medicine would make my hair fall out as well. I thought, you're only joking. It was only when I started having it and my hair started falling out that I started going mad. My hair was falling out! It was really long, down below my shoulders.'

For her this was, and always has been, the worst part of cancer treatment. A photograph of Jaymee on her sixth birthday, the month before her cancer was diagnosed, shows her with beautiful, long, dark brown hair. Within a few weeks of the treatment starting, it had all gone.

It happened gradually. First a few strands, then one morning when she woke up, the hair was matted all over her pillow. Whatever strength of mind Jaymee's unconventional childhood had given her, she wasn't prepared for this. She started pulling it out. 'It doesn't hurt at all, you just hear sounds like pulling cotton wool from a big bunch and then you go and look in the mirror and you see it's all come out. It's devastating, you know, losing your hair. Just think of it as when you go out in the snow. Your head feels very cold. Try to imagine it being like that every day and that your hair at the moment is a hat that you have to wear. Try and imagine it being like that and then try and imagine forgetting to put your hat on one day, going outside and it's like snow. Or to put it more bluntly, just try and imagine sticking your head in a freezer. You've got no protection whatsoever.' Over the last five years, Jaymee has lost her hair four times.

During those first few weeks at Addenbrooke's, Jaymee was, according to various members of the family, 'very very low'. As if losing her hair wasn't bad enough, she also had to cope with the discomfort of the drip which administered her drugs at precise and regular intervals through a tube which had been inserted into her wrist.

For a six-year-old, the experience was terrifying. 'When I saw the size of the needle they were going to stick in me, I wouldn't let them come near me,' Jaymee said. 'They were going to put it in my hand and I wouldn't let them touch me. Eventually they got to stick it in me and it hurt like anything. They said they couldn't give me the medicine in tablets or anything else, so it had to be this way.'

The constant presence of the little portable trolley to which her drip bags were attached made her reluctant to get up and move about because she had to trail it behind her wherever she went, and she was frightened in case one of the bags emptied or fell off, setting off an alarm. 'When you're attached to all these things, you don't really feel like doing much because you think, I've got to take this thing with me and walk such a long way to the playroom. What if it bleeps, what am I going to do, it's just too much hassle, it's not worth it.'

As well as the constant presence of the drip bags, Jaymee had to put up with the distressing side-effects of chemotherapy which made life in hospital even harder to bear. 'Chemotherapy can make you feel a lot of things. It can make you feel tired, it can make you feel like you have to go to the toilet a lot more often than normal. It can put you off your food altogether and it can make you feel sick.'

To try to counteract the nausea, Jaymee was given anti-sickness drugs. But they had the opposite effect, and there were days when she seemed to vomit constantly. At other times Jaymee would ask one of the play nurses to read her a story to help send her to sleep for a few hours while she was having the chemotherapy, hoping that by the time she woke the nausea would have passed. 'After that I'd feel up to getting up and doing something, so I'd get up and play a game, probably eat, then read some more and go to bed.'

Debbie stayed in hospital with her most of the time even though she was expecting her second child at any moment. They were given a family room so that James, Charlotte and David could come and stay when they could. David was away working for much of the time, leaving Debbie in charge of the children.

'Daddy would stay sometimes, but not nearly as much as he does now,' Jaymee said. 'Out of a month, he would stay two or three days.' That meant that some days Jaymee was left on her own. 'I had all the nurses and they were all very friendly. They had a big selection of films and they'd let me go in the teenage room and watch them by myself. I didn't really get lonely because I had friends on the ward I could hang about with.'

Three weeks after the treatment began, she was allowed to go home for a few days. It was perfect timing. Debbie went into labour and gave birth to another boy, Alexander, in Newmarket Hospital. Then she took the baby back to Addenbrooke's with her so that she could stay with Jaymee as the next phase of her treatment began. It was a difficult time for all of them.

The atmosphere on a children's cancer ward is an extraordinary mixture of despair and hope. During the time Debbie spent with Jaymee in Addenbrooke's, she would watch other young children wander up and down the corridor pulling their drip trolleys behind them like huge toy dumpertrucks, apparently oblivious to their illness, and marvel at their courage. At other times she would hear them crying, sometimes screaming, in pain.

When Jaymee felt well enough she would go and visit other children in their rooms or go and join one of the classes which took place in the playroom every day. Everyone had their own strategy for passing the time. 'They had school from nine to twelve and then there was a whole six hours of play. At tea-time it closes and you would eat your tea in there, but the room would close at six so after that you're stuck with TV or you borrow a few games to bring back tomorrow.'

According to her family, Jaymee was 'wonderful' at making friends in hospital. Although she hadn't been told exactly what was wrong with her, it was perfectly obvious that she was surrounded by other children who were seriously ill. And that made her think.

'You don't realize that they're worse than you. You just see them with bigger plasters and you think, What's happened to them? But it makes the situation difficult for you because you're wondering if this is going to happen to you. You might get something that no one knows anything about. So it puts a lot of pressure on you because you start worrying about the pain of what might come, because the treatment does hurt.

And in hospitals you find it very hard to be happy in a place like that.'

It wasn't only fear that Jaymee remembers feeling the first time she was ill. She was angry, not with other people but with herself. She says she often wanted to kick herself because she couldn't think who else to vent her feelings on.

Jaymee went home from hospital in the New Year, after recovering from a bout of pneumonia she had picked up because her resistance to infection was so low after the chemotherapy. When she was well enough, Debbie had a choice to make: either she could keep Jaymee at home until her hair had grown back, or she could send her back to school so that she could live as normal a life as possible. Jaymee was anxious to get back and see her schoolfriends. But she was completely unprepared for their reaction.

'I went back to school and I started wearing a baseball cap because I was embarrassed about my hair, and I'd go out into the playground and people would take it off. They'd throw it about and take it away.'

Her teachers seemed powerless to prevent what to Jaymee was something akin to torture. 'They were told not to tease me but they just didn't stop. It was funny seeing a girl with no hair. They thought I was different. They would tease me really badly.'

Five years later, the pain is still there in Jaymee's face when she talks about it. 'I began to wonder who I could trust because the people who were teasing me were the people that I thought were my friends before all this had happened. I thought, I've obviously done something wrong. I've had enough punishment, don't you think? Then you start thinking, What did I do to deserve this? I think, basically, they just didn't understand it, didn't know how to handle it.'

In hospital, where everyone had understood her predicament, Jaymee had been cocooned from the outside world, with all her attention focused on getting through the treatment so that she could go back to school. Suddenly, the outside world seemed a particularly cruel place to be in, and for the first time Jaymee began to wonder what had happened to her and whether she would ever be the same again. After everything she had been through, it was a harsh awakening.

3

A Precarious Balance

There were other problems on the horizon too. David and Debbie's marriage was on the point of breaking down. In 1991 David had started a relationship with a woman called Susan Manning who lived nearby and had two sons of her own from her first marriage. He was still living with Debbie, however, and eventually she decided that if David wouldn't leave and the relationship with Susan was going to continue, she would have to go herself. But she knew that would mean leaving Jaymee and Charlotte behind, and after all they had been through together, that was the most difficult decision to make. She would have liked to take the girls with her: by now they were like her own daughters. But she knew that not only did she have no right to take them, but David would never give them up, however much she had been a mother to them.

Without telling anyone what she was planning to do, Debbie took her two sons, James and Alexander, and left home one day in November 1991. Her departure came as a complete shock to Jaymee and Charlotte. Debbie had dropped them off at school that morning and they had expected her to pick them up at the end of the afternoon. Instead, Debbie's mother came to collect them. 'Gran said Mummy had gone out, she'd be back later,' Jaymee said. 'She never showed up. Then Daddy came to collect us from Gran's house and said that Mummy would be back tomorrow. I didn't see her for ages after that. Dad said she was staying with a friend.'

Eventually David did take the girls back to Debbie, who was now living in Northamptonshire. 'He took us down there with our stuff and helped us move in and moved his stuff in too, but he was hardly ever there,' Jaymee said. 'He nearly missed James's birthday and mine because he was spending time with Susan.' Jaymee was furious with her father for allowing Debbie to leave. 'I knew Mummy must have left because of Susan because she just wouldn't walk out over nothing,' she said. 'When your parents split up, it's like your life is just over. Childhood can't get more complicated than that. A life-threatening illness, a new girlfriend living in your house with two children, what else can you pile on top to make it worse?'

This is Jaymee at her bleakest, a side of her which rarely shows because she has learned to keep her feelings to herself. But it is hardly surprising that her relationship with her father is so complex. In the last year he has championed her cause to the limit, yet there have been times in her life when he simply hasn't been around.

'Then I've just had to grit my teeth and bear it myself or go and look for help somewhere else,' she said. Yet Jaymee has also come to depend on David because, apart from her grandparents, he remains the only relatively constant presence in her life. 'I've learned not to rely on anyone except Daddy because he'll stay the same. Other people come and go.'

At times, when asked about the effect his emotional life has had on his children, David appears curiously complacent. 'I probably won't gauge the effect fully until later in their lives, but I think they'll cope,' he said. 'I mean, Jaymee has had to cope with far bigger hurdles in her life and I think she's come through OK. I think Jaymee and Charlotte will have learnt from their experiences and I hope it will make them slightly better people. They don't suffer from the delusion that everything is perfect in this world.'

At other times, particularly when Jaymee has been ill, he has had to ask himself tougher questions. 'You feel you have let your child down and you start to search for reasons and wonder if she's being punished for something I've done. Could I have made her life happier? Is it because of the strain or stress I've put her through? Should I have stayed with Debbie? It's an enormous guilt trip.'

When David and Debbie split up, Jaymee was only halfway through her treatment at Addenbrooke's, although her cancer was still in remission and she was able to go to school. The treatment continued until August 1992, when the particular clinical 'protocol' she had been put on came to an end. After that, all the family could do was to hope that Jaymee's leukaemia had been cured.

Leukaemia is the most common form of cancer in children. About 450 new cases are diagnosed every year. Because of the advances in chemotherapy, more than 60 per cent of children who develop it between the ages of two and fifteen now recover fully and lead perfectly normal lives. The chance of a long-lasting cure depends on how effectively the cancer cells respond to drugs. The more resistant they are, the less likelihood there is of a long-term cure. As with most diseases, finding the most effective treatment can take many years. Different combinations and types of drugs have to be tried and tested in exactly the same way on large numbers of patients in clinical trials before doctors can say with certainty that a particular kind of treatment works. The course of treatment Jaymee's doctors believed was right for her had been devised as a new clinical trial, begun in 1990 – the year she was diagnosed – and due to last five years, after which the results would be evaluated. It was called Protocol NHL 904.

Because so many of the drugs used to treat cancer are relatively new, it is not always possible to assess the extent of any long-term damage they might cause. All the doctors can say with reasonable certainty is that the drugs appear to offer a good chance of cure or at least long-term remission from the disease. When the alternative is certain death, they believe most parents would want to take that chance.

What children's cancer specialists are more reluctant to tell parents at a stage where they are still recovering from the shock of being told that their child has cancer, is that there is a risk that the anti-cancer drugs themselves might cause their child to develop another form of cancer later on. The risk is small compared with a potential cure rate of anything up to 80 per cent – but it is significant. With some types of drug the risk is even higher. Both David and Debbie are adamant that they had not understood the risks that might be involved in Jaymee's treatment.

Doctors admit the decision about how much information to give parents about potential risks is extremely difficult at a time when they are clinging desperately to the hope that their child will be cured. 'I think the risk of causing a second cancer is the most difficult thing to tell parents,' said Dr Simon Meller, a children's cancer specialist at the Royal Marsden Hospital, one of the country's leading cancer hospitals. 'I don't think any sensible person would deprive their child of a chance of cure from that first cancer provided the risk is reasonably small.'

The dilemma becomes even more acute when what seems to be the most effective drug available also has a higher-than-average chance of causing another cancer. What do the doctors do then? 'Should a doctor deprive a patient of an effective drug because it may have a higher risk of causing second cancers if it is more effective than the alternatives?' said Simon Meller. 'What is a doctor's first priority? To do his very best to cure the cancer he's got in front of him at all costs.'

In Jaymee's case, the two years' treatment she received at Addenbrooke's Hospital seemed to have worked – her cancer was still in remission and her hair had grown back to its previous length. But then in December 1993, despite these months of chemical warfare waged against the cancer, and after only fifteen months' normality, Jaymee's leukaemia came back, shattering the Bowens' hopes all over again. David remembers seeing the tell-tale bruising, a signal that all was not right in Jaymee's blood. 'When Jaymee put a glass to her mouth and sucked the air out of it, like children do, the imprint of the glass stayed fixed on her face. When she took the glass off, the red mark went black and blue and stood there like she'd put make-up on, with a circle where the glass had been. And that was the first clue that she had a problem.'

He took her back to Addenbrooke's Hospital for tests. Three hours later he was telephoned at work. 'They told me there were some abnormalities in Jaymee's blood and they wanted to discuss the situation with me. This time I was a little bit quicker on my feet and I knew what they were talking about. They hadn't telephoned me once in two years, so I knew it was going to be bad news.'

He was right. This time it was a different type of the disease – acute myeloid leukaemia (AML) – and much more difficult to treat. Whether it had been caused by the drugs she'd been given to tackle the first cancer will never be known for sure – but at least one of her doctors believes it was.

One of the drugs included in Jaymee's initial chemotherapy was etoposide, one of a group of anti-cancer drugs which began to be used on children in the 1980s. An article in the

British Medical Journal in April 1992 concluded that such drugs seemed to be involved in secondary leukaemia after childhood cancer, with a slightly higher incidence among non-Hodgkin's lymphomas.

But it was not until many months later that David learned of its possible involvement in Jaymee's relapse. All he knew at the time was that what Jaymee had now – acute myeloid leukaemia – was much more resistant to drugs and much more difficult to cure. She had also developed a chromosomal abnormality, one of the classic hallmarks of treatment-related leukaemia. There are about seventy new cases of AML diagnosed in children every year in the UK. About half can expect to be cured. In Jaymee's case, the odds were stacked against her even more because this was the second time she'd developed cancer.

When the doctor at Addenbrooke's Hospital broke the news to David that Jaymee's cancer had come back, Jaymee was in the room with her father. 'I'd got into the habit of not listening to the doctor very often because she'd say something and then she'd go into this big long speech about what it was and stuff. So I'd just sit there and look like I was listening and say "yes, yes, yes" to everything.'

But this time she began to realize that something was wrong and that she should be listening to what the doctor was saying. 'At the time, I remember looking at the doctor and she said something about a bone marrow transplant and Daddy said, "What are the chances of survival?" And that question just made me look at him and he was crying, or his eyes were really red and they really had a lot of water in them. And I'm thinking, Did I miss something here? When I heard the word survival, I sort of just clicked – I should be listening to this. Survival, this means big time.'

It was the first time Jaymee could ever remember David looking worried. 'It's a good thing this man's really good at hiding his feelings,' she said later. 'It's one of the things he's good at. Sometimes it works to his advantage, sometimes it doesn't.'

Jaymee's doctors told David that despite the intensive chemotherapy Jaymee had been given, it had failed to stop her producing cancer cells which her own immune system was unable to kill off. The only option now was to give her stronger and more toxic drugs to attack the leukaemic cells. This would be combined with a treatment called total body irradiation which would completely destroy Jaymee's own bone marrow and immune system, so that she could be given a bone marrow transplant, replacing her marrow with that from a donor. If it worked, it would also boost Jaymee's immune system, giving her the ammunition to fight off any new leukaemia cells which threatened to attack. It is a treatment of last resort.

But before a transplant could even be considered, a donor had to be found whose genetic make-up would mean their bone marrow was a suitable match for Jaymee's. The best donors are usually brothers and sisters. David and Susan had had a little girl called Phoebe, born earlier that year, so Jaymee now had four siblings. But the only real hope of finding a good match was from a brother or sister who shared the same parents. After waiting patiently in the wings, Charlotte suddenly found herself in the spotlight for the first time. Everyone's hopes for Jaymee's survival were pinned on the composition of her blood. If Charlotte wasn't a suitable donor, it would mean searching the national and perhaps even international bone marrow registers for an alternative, a process which could take weeks and could well end in failure.

But Jaymee was lucky. 'A few days later they came back and said, David, we've got a match,' Charlotte remembered. 'I thought, "Oh good, at least I'm appreciated now." Then he said, "Charlotte, you wouldn't mind going to hospital, would you?" I asked what would happen and he said, "You're going to have a needle in your back." He said, "Jaymee needs it." '

Ever since Jaymee's illness, Charlotte had felt that she had had to take second place in the Bowen household. Now she was to play a major role in trying to save her sister's life and it meant that, for a while at least, she would be the centre of attention.

Jaymee and Charlotte are very different in character and appearance. Even if Jaymee had remained healthy, Charlotte might well have found herself competing for attention from her father. David and Jaymee share a quick-wittedness which makes them formidable sparring partners. When they argue, which they frequently do, neither gives up easily and David respects Jaymee's logical mind. With her dark skin, Jaymee and David look much more alike than David and Charlotte, whose skin is white and whose hair is straight. She looks more like her mother, and her personality is less abrasive than that of her father and sister. Charlotte likes to play the fool, whereas Jaymee is more serious and contemplative.

Charlotte was not yet five when Jaymee's cancer was first diagnosed, but the memory of her early days in hospital is still strong. 'I can remember Jaymee crying, "Daddy, I don't like this," ' she said. When Jaymee was ill, Charlotte says she felt forgotten. 'I wanted to know why Jaymee was getting so much attention when I was the youngest and I should be getting it.' When Jaymee was at home, she and Charlotte shared a bedroom. 'We had bunk beds. She was at the top and I was at the bottom. I would just stare at the bedsprings above me and then I would start kicking them with both feet.'

'It's a by-product of what happens when you've got one ill child,' David admitted. 'However hard you try, you're going to divert your love and care and attention on a larger percentage basis to the one who's ill, so the one who's not ill suffers. I haven't found a sensible solution to that. I try but I haven't found one, I don't believe one exists.'

Yet Jaymee and Charlotte are fiercely protective of each other, something David has tried to make the most of when Jaymee has been at her worst. 'Charlotte is like a tonic. She picks you up. She makes you laugh. She does silly things. She's a breath of fresh air which you need to keep Jaymee going. Charlotte is one of the things that pulls Jaymee through but Jaymee doesn't know it. If Charlotte wasn't there, Jaymee would really be in deep trouble.'

Charlotte had an innate confidence in her sister which boosted everyone's morale. 'I knew she wasn't going to die,' she said. 'I was too young to understand what damage leukaemia could do. Jaymee never talked about it, she just got on with life as normal. She didn't complain unless she really hated something. There was one medicine she hated and it's all chalky but she has to have it and Dad said, "You have to have it because if you don't you won't get better," and she said, "If I do have it I probably won't get better anyway." '

Between the time Jaymee's leukaemia returned, in December 1993, and her bone marrow transplant the following March, she spent most of her time in hospital. The first stage of her treatment was more chemotherapy to try to get her cancer into remission. Once again, Jaymee found herself back on the children's cancer ward at Addenbrooke's Hospital.

It meant losing her precious hair again just when it had all grown back. Having been through it once made it much worse. 'I was leaning on my pillow and I'd noticed that the back of my head was very cold and I just got an itch there, so I put my hand back to scratch and I couldn't feel any hair. And I got a really bad shock and I went to the nurse and I said, "Can you tell me if there's any hair there?" and she said, "No, there isn't." I just went back to my bed and cried.'

Jaymee says she didn't realize that she was going to lose her hair again and hadn't prepared herself. 'Children should at least be told that their hair is going to fall out,' she said. 'They have a right to know everything.' Just how far those rights should extend was the issue David would have to confront later on. Meanwhile there were the practicalities of Jaymee's treatment to consider.

This time, she was given a special tube called a Hickman line, which allowed the doctors to inject drugs straight into her body without the use of needles. The line was inserted, under anaesthetic, beneath the skin of Jaymee's chest, with one end feeding directly into a large blood vessel around her heart. The other end, left outside her chest, had several different valves to which the drip bags containing all her drugs could be attached. Not only was it less painful than using needles, it also meant that doctors had an instantly accessible route through which to get drugs into her system if there was a crisis.

When her treatment was over, Jaymee's line would be removed, leaving a small scar. But for a nine-year-old child, the prospect of having a line permanently sticking out of her chest was daunting. 'It is actually quite frightening. Before I had my first line in I was being told, come on, it's not that bad. And then I saw these two children with them in already and I thought, well, it can't really be that bad, but I still needed quite a lot of convincing and in the end I just went with it because even if I did say no, the doctors were going to put it in anyway. It turned out to be OK. You have to be careful with it though, because if it gets caught between your legs and you're trying to stand up it doesn't half hurt!'

While Jaymee was in remission this time, she made friends with a boy called Luke. He was a year younger than her and was also suffering from leukaemia. Luke was given a bone marrow transplant too, but eventually he died. Both Jaymee and Charlotte were desperately upset. Jaymee says Luke's death made her wonder if her leukaemia would kill her too, but by then it was in remission, so the fear was not quite so immediate.

The bone marrow transplant Jaymee now faced would be even tougher than the ordeal she'd already been through. She would need all the love and support her family could give her and, since her first illness, the composition of that family had changed significantly. To Jaymee, the really important difference between this time and last time in hospital was that she was no longer living with Debbie. In November, just one month before Jaymee's leukaemia came back, David had moved Jaymee and Charlotte away from Debbie's house and taken them to live with Susan. It was difficult for Jaymee to accept that the woman she thought of as her mother had been replaced, but Debbie tried to be as supportive as possible. As soon as she heard that Jaymee had relapsed, she went straight to the hospital to be with her.

Jaymee had to spend Christmas in hospital that year because her resistance to infection was so low after her chemotherapy. It was a traumatic time for them all. On Christmas Day, it was Susan and her children who went to the hospital, not Debbie. 'Christmas wasn't much fun,' Charlotte said. 'The TV was switched off at eight and we had to be in bed by nine. Santa Claus came and Phoebe sat on his lap. Everyone on the ward came and sat down for Christmas dinner together, including the people on drips. There were people in there who looked much iller than Jaymee.'

But that wasn't all. On Christmas Eve Jaymee had had another upset. Without telling anyone, Susan had got in touch with Alyson and told her that Jaymee was ill. It was the first time Alyson had known anything about Jaymee's cancer and her immediate response was to visit her daughter in hospital. Without warning, the woman whom Jaymee still thought of as her aunt appeared at her bedside wanting to talk to her. When David arrived at the hospital, he was furious.

'She caused a great fuss,' Jaymee said. 'Well, if you had a child who was sick, she's got a splitting headache and a cold and you barge through the door and you start with the father in front of the child, what are you supposed to think?'

Six days later, Alyson came to the hospital again. Jaymee was confused and upset by her presence and couldn't under-stand why this woman seemed to know so much about her. It was to be another year before she learned the truth, but, for now, these meetings simply made Jaymee's time in hospital more difficult to bear.

She had had one course of chemotherapy and, like the first time, her leukaemia had immediately gone into remission. After Christmas she would have another dose to make sure any remaining cancer cells were destroyed. It needed all Jaymee's willpower to get through it, and then there was the transplant to be faced.

When her doctors had discussed the possibility of a bone marrow transplant with David, they had been frank about her chances of survival. 'They said it was 40 per cent,' David said. 'You can't sum up how frightened you are, and you do the best you can because you know that if you don't the other option is certain death.'

4

Transplant

Jaymee was to have her bone marrow transplant at the Royal Marsden Hospital near Croydon, one of Britain's leading specialist centres for the treatment of leukaemia in children. There was an added bonus too. The hospital was very near Ossie and Rita's house, so Jaymee would have the constant support of her grandparents during the difficult weeks ahead.

The countdown to Jaymee's bone marrow transplant began on Tuesday 15 March 1994 when she was admitted to the Royal Marsden's children's cancer unit for preliminary tests and an explanation of what the transplant would involve. She would be given another dose of chemotherapy, followed by an intensive course of radiation over a period of several days.

This would prepare her body for the transplant by getting rid of her diseased bone marrow and eliminating her own immune system so that it would not reject Charlotte's marrow when it was given to her. Because she was going to be given so many different drugs, Jaymee was given another Hickman line. Then she was allowed home for ten days before the treatment began. Once she was back in hospital she was likely to have to stay there for at least a month.

The children's cancer unit at the Royal Marsden is designed to look as unimposing as possible. There are friezes and children's pictures on the walls, a specially designed low reception desk in the outpatient department so that children do not feel they are being stared down at from a great height by the medical staff behind the desk, separate playrooms for small children where play 'specialists' help introduce children to the treatment which lies ahead and encourage them to voice their fears, and a team of nurses specially trained in child psychology and children's cancer.

Because children can expect to be in hospital for many weeks, parents usually move in with them. A kitchen, laundry room and sitting area beside the children's ward have been allocated specifically to them to try and make them feel as comfortable as possible and also to provide them with space which is theirs rather than obliging them to mix with the medical staff at all times.

This time, David was taking no chances. He stayed with Jaymee throughout the entire period she was in hospital. He was the only father staying with his child, and was surrounded by mothers. 'You see them every day and you see them when you wake up in the morning, you see them at night without make-up on. Then you become pally with them. Your room becomes a sanctuary, like your own little house,' he said.

To begin with, he says, the women found it strange to have him in their midst, but gradually he got to know them. 'It was interesting because I've never been one for frivolous conversation, but when you're there in hospital the one thing that you can all talk about is your child's illness and you can help each other out and find information out.'

When Jaymee arrived back at the Royal Marsden, there were four days to go before the transplant. She was started on the high-dose chemotherapy immediately and two days later was given the first of six doses of total body irradiation. Jaymee hated it. 'I went into this room and they drew crosses on my back and on my front and told me not to wash them off. Then they put little pads on the crosses and made me sit in this little plastic container; then they'd clip little metal clips to the pads and make me lie first on my back and then on my front, and it really hurt. It's very boring – you've got to lie in fixed positions and they come and change your position every half-hour. I found it easier if I managed to fall asleep.' Jaymee had to endure this procedure twice a day for the next three days.

The day before the transplant, Charlotte was admitted to hospital too, to prepare for her bone marrow 'harvest'. Just before she was given the infusion of Charlotte's marrow, Jaymee would be having the final dose of radiation to make sure that nothing remained of her own immune system. This would give Charlotte's bone marrow the best possible chance of being accepted by Jaymee's body. It was medical choreography of the highest order.

The night before the transplant Jaymee and Charlotte shared a room. Everyone knew the transplant procedure would be more painful for Charlotte than for Jaymee. She had to have the marrow removed under anaesthetic. Two needles were placed in the back of her hip bone and a mixture of marrow and blood sucked up into syringes. Then the mixture was put into sterile drip bags and given to Jaymee through her Hickman line, just like an ordinary blood transfusion.

Before the transplant David had teased Jaymee about the personality change she would be certain to undergo as a result of getting Charlotte's bone marrow. 'At the time,' Jaymee said, 'I remember thinking, "Oh why does it have to be her, why can't it be someone else?" '

After Charlotte's marrow had been removed, David brought her into Jaymee's room, where she lay curled up on the end of Jaymee's bed while her sister was being given the transplant.

After it was all over, Jaymee and Charlotte had one of their most typical sisterly discussions. 'I remember having an argument with her and she said, "Well, you've got lots of little me's inside you now,"' Jaymee recalled. 'I said, "Excuse me, this is your bone marrow we're talking about here, not your brain cells." And she said, "Well, I gave it to you." I said, "I don't want it," and she said, "Well, I'll have it back then." So I said, "Well, it's a bit late now, isn't it!"'

Ten days later, when her body's ability to resist infection was at its lowest, with the combined effect of the onslaught of chemotherapy and radiation, Jaymee went into isolation. The sterile, protected environment felt like a prison cell.

'You're in a room with a bed, a chair, a fridge, a couple of wardrobes, a TV, a window and a bathroom. Every time someone enters the room they have to go through this whole system. You have to go into a special washing room, wash your hands, wash your face and any skin that's been out in the air. You have to put on a hat so any bugs in your hair don't get out, and you have to put on an apron to make sure that nothing gets on your clothes. When they leave they have to take it all off and throw it away.'

Jaymee was not allowed to leave the room at all. Most of the time, she says, the door was bolted shut. 'You can't get out of this room. The only two ways you can see out are through a little glass window in the door and the window to the outside of the hospital.'

Jaymee was in isolation for ten days and, apart from the nurses, only David and Ossie were allowed in the room during that time. David slept in the room with her. In spite of their almost constant squabbles, it was at times like this that David felt Charlotte could be of most help to Jaymee. But because her sister was in isolation, Charlotte was restricted to communicating with her through the door of her room.

'I tried to persuade Dad to let me go in and see her,' Charlotte said. 'I said, "I can help a lot, she can break my hand if she wants to squeeze it." I wanted to be in that room, I knew she would have liked me in there so she could have talked to me, called me stupid and twit-face and ugly.'

Every day Jaymee was in hospital, Ossie and Rita would come and visit. Rita would try to bring whatever Jaymee wanted to eat so that she had something to look forward to. Their constant presence and support helped keep David sane.

'I had a lot of support from visitors, relatives, friends and even some of the nurses from Addenbrooke's,' he said. 'If you had to be in hospital, then I suppose it was as pleasant a place as you could have wished to be in. But at the end of the day it is still soul-destroying. One day blurs into the next and you can't remember what you did the day before or even what day it is.'

However tough it was, it was worth it. The doctors were astonished at how well Jaymee responded to the transplant. She was being given special drugs to help ensure that her body didn't reject Charlotte's marrow, and after ten days in isolation she was allowed out and back on to the children's ward. She was discharged on 18 April, just over three weeks after she'd been admitted, the shortest length of time any of the Royal Marsden's patients had had to stay after a transplant.

Jaymee went to stay with Ossie and Rita for the next two months so that she could continue being monitored by the Royal Marsden. David and Charlotte stayed with her for most of the time. Jaymee says she felt anxious and uncertain during that period, feelings which are not uncommon after a bone marrow transplant. Recent studies suggest that many of the feelings which children experience after a transplant are similar to those of people suffering from post-traumatic stress syndrome.

'You know that if you've been in hospital you might never be the same again,' Jaymee said. 'Some of those drugs can really affect you. Because I had radiation in the Royal Marsden my defence system was totally destroyed, and when you don't have one, you have to build it up as your life goes on and now I have to start like a baby. Start again.'

For Jaymee, there were the added complications of her family life. According to one study:

> There was a clear relationship between the children's adjustment after bone marrow transplant and the influence of their social environment. In the first place, the adjustment of the children was related to the emotional state of their parents (in particular the mothers) and their marital happiness. Stable parental support has been seen as essential for the patient's coping with the illness and hospitalization.*

On the face of it, the emotional odds seemed to be stacked against Jaymee. But she also had an extraordinary resilience which, according to the same study, would have helped her too:

> The children who made a better adjustment after [a bone marrow transplant] tended to have some kind of 'buffer'. This seemed to consist of the appropriate use of defence mechanisms, in particular denial, and of resilience, developed through previous stressful experiences.

When Jaymee eventually went back to school after her transplant, she was given a very different welcome from the last time she had appeared with no hair. Since her first illness Jaymee had moved schools. Now she was at a school called Scaltback, where her classmates knew about her illness and understood that sometimes she would have hair and sometimes she wouldn't. 'When I went back to Scaltback and I took my hat off, no one looked at me, no one was actually

---

* *The Psychosocial Effects of Bone Marrow Transplantation in Children* by Carien Pot-Mees (Eburon-Delft, 1989).

that bothered, so I just left it off,' Jaymee said. 'It made me more confident knowing that my friends wouldn't actually laugh at me.'

'They knew she had leukaemia. Jaymee used to tell the class about her experiences,' said her form teacher, Felicia Goss, whom Jaymee had come to trust, and who felt particularly sympathetic to all that she had been through. Felicia could see immediately that although Jaymee was only nine, she was dealing with someone much older and wiser than her years. 'She appeared to be more like a sixteen-year-old and was very grown-up compared with the rest of the class. She'd want to stay in at break times and help me rather than go out and play with the other children, and she talked to me like an adult.'

Jaymee knew that her experiences had set her apart from other children. She knew that they could never begin to understand what she had been through, so it was easier to talk to the grown-ups. She also had an extraordinary thirst for knowledge and even though she had missed a great deal of school as a result of her illness, never found it difficult to catch up. 'She was certainly of above-average intelligence and very well read,' Felicia said. 'She liked nothing better than to work and always asked lots of questions.'

And Jaymee was very much her father's daughter – questioning, alert, analytical and, like David, not someone who enjoyed 'frivolous' conversation. The combination of that and the maturity she had gained as a result of her illness made Jaymee Bowen a formidable character.

'There was always a barrier between her and other people; she didn't like to get close to them,' Felicia said. Perhaps that was as much a question of survival tactics as a genuine aloofness. Jaymee's experiences had taught her to be on her guard. She never knew what might happen next. If she hid her feelings, she was less likely to get hurt. The months following her bone marrow transplant were a time of mixed emotions for David too. Jaymee's body seemed to have taken to the transplant well, better than anyone had hoped, but it was still very early days and she had to make regular visits to Addenbrooke's, who had taken over responsibility for her care once again.

'You sit there thinking, What if something goes wrong?' said David. 'The illusion as far as the public is concerned is that life is normal, but as a parent this is your worst time because you're just in the lap of the gods. You're not in hospital, you're not actively fighting the disease; but once you have found out that your child has leukaemia and it's come back, the only thing that can happen is that you treat it again and they either survive or they don't.'

Talk of 'curing' cancer is always fraught with caveats. Technically, you are considered cured if the disease has not come back after five years. But who is to say it will not reappear five years and one week later? It is not surprising that patients and their families are frequently left with the feeling of living on borrowed time. When the cancer has already returned once, the concept of 'cure' has even less meaning. Then a year's survival, or even less, is considered to be a bonus.

By September 1994, five months after her transplant, Jaymee's cancer was still in remission, her hair was growing back and she was well enough to spend nearly all her time at school. David decided he wanted to take the children to America for a much-needed holiday, so in December the family went to Florida and visited Disney World with the help of funding from a charity for sick children. When they came home it was almost Christmas, the first Christmas Jaymee would have enjoyed entirely away from hospital since the start of her illness five years before. They spent it at Susan's house and, according to Jaymee, 'It was a nice Christmas.'

It was now eight months since the transplant. 'A false sense of security, that's what it is. That's the problem,' David said. 'You sit there and think, She's all right. And then, of course, out of the blue it hits you again. You have no contingency plans, no nothing.'

5

Time to Let Go?

It was Tuesday 17 January 1995, Charlotte's ninth birthday. The family were hoping to make it a special celebration. The previous year, her birthday party had taken place in the children's cancer unit at Addenbrooke's Hospital, where Jaymee was having chemotherapy to prepare her for her bone marrow transplant. Although everyone had made an effort and brought presents and party food, it wasn't the same as celebrating your birthday at home.

This year, it was going to be different. Rita had bought Charlotte a 'Mr Blobby' cake and taken it up to David's house the weekend before, along with some presents for her. Throughout the day she noticed that Jaymee looked tired and rather pale and spent most of her time sitting in an armchair, preferring to eat her meals there rather than getting up to sit at the table. Rita was worried. When Jaymee was well, she had much more energy than this, but there didn't seem to be any immediate cause for concern. Jaymee's recent tests at Addenbrooke's had showed that she was doing well and that her leukaemia was still in remission.

It was now nine months since her bone marrow transplant and, as each month passed, the family had become more optimistic about her chance of survival. They knew that the longer the cancer remained in remission, the better the chance of success.

But on the morning of Charlotte's birthday the Bowens'

world began to fall apart for the third time. Four days earlier David had taken Jaymee to Addenbrooke's for a routine blood test. On the morning of Charlotte's birthday, a letter arrived from Addenbrooke's with the results. It was short and to the point. The hospital had detected some 'abnormalities' in Jaymee's blood and her platelets were low. Could David bring her back to Addenbrooke's as soon as possible? He knew exactly what the letter meant. Earlier that week Jaymee had coughed up some blood on her pillow when she woke up.

David said nothing. He didn't want to upset the girls. He would take Jaymee back to Addenbrooke's the next day. That way it would just seem like a normal visit. Charlotte had two friends round for a birthday tea as they'd planned, but David didn't feel like celebrating: 17 January 1995 is a day he would rather forget.

The following day, Jaymee and David set off for the hospital. Jaymee had no idea there was any cause for alarm because David was adopting his tried and tested method of keeping his emotions to himself. 'If you don't look upset, there's nothing to worry about, is there?' Jaymee said. 'If you don't look upset, there's no reason for anyone to get suspicious.'

'She had a couple of tests and they kept us waiting and then they came back and took some more blood and then went off again,' David said. 'By that time I already knew, because all they were doing was checking it.'

He was right. The results came through and David was called into one of the doctors' offices. 'She told me that Jaymee had relapsed and that there was nothing more they could do. I said what about another bone marrow transplant and they said they didn't think it would work. I knew that the situation was hopeless as far as they were concerned.'

David rang his father straight away. 'David telephoned me in tears,' Ossie said. 'He could hardly speak. He said: "Dad, they say there's been a relapse. They can't do anything. She's going to die."'

Ossie telephoned Rita at work immediately and told her he would pick her up in five minutes. Together they set off for the hospital because they knew from the sound of David's voice on the telephone that he needed help.

It was a day no parent could ever forget. Two years earlier David had been told that Jaymee's chance of survival was slim. Since that day he had never given up hope. His faith in Jaymee's ability to overcome the odds had been unshakeable. Now the doctors who had been trying to cure Jaymee for the last five years were telling him there was nothing more they could do. To give Jaymee any more aggressive treatment would only be delaying the inevitable and wouldn't be in her best interests.

'We really hit a low point then,' Rita told me. Rita is a regular churchgoer, but the following Sunday she told Ossie she wasn't going. She couldn't see the point. Her faith had deserted her. It took her several weeks, and a visit from the vicar she had known for years, to convince her it was worth going back.

Two days after they'd been told that Jaymee had relapsed, David and Ossie had a meeting with Valerie Broadbent, who had been away at a conference when Jaymee's test results came back. Dr Broadbent had been in charge of Jaymee's care for the last five years. But her notes of the discussion with David make it clear that as far as she was concerned, there was now nothing more she could do. They simply said: 'Bone marrow shows a relapse of AML. There is now no curative treatment.'

After five years during which he had been told there were always alternatives available to try and cure his daughter,

David was told that palliative care was now the only realistic option. That meant keeping her symptoms at bay for as long as possible and, as time went on, using doses of morphine to control the pain she would suffer in her joints. But giving her more aggressive treatment, such as chemotherapy, was, they said, out of the question.

David asked Dr Broadbent how much time Jaymee had. She told him it wouldn't take long. Most of the bone marrow which had been transplanted from Charlotte had already been invaded by cancer cells and they were multiplying fast. At most, she had eight weeks to live.

'It was the single most upsetting moment in my entire life. I don't think that there's anything anyone can do to me that's going to faze me as much as that fazed me. It really rocked me,' David said. 'I couldn't believe that my daughter had spent half of her life in and out of hospitals being treated for a disease, being supported by doctors who all of a sudden say, "Well, OK, this is too much. Sorry, chaps."'

David went straight from the hospital to Jaymee's school, where he had a meeting with the headteacher, David Pugh. 'He was very distressed,' Mr Pugh said. 'The news had come as an enormous shock to him, as indeed it was to us because right up until that time Jaymee had been, apparently, in the best of health. Obviously we knew she'd had leukaemia, obviously we knew she'd had treatment. But she was back in school, fit, smiling, untroubled by illness, and so it came as a bolt from the blue.'

Struggling to come to terms with what the doctors had said, David had a decision to make. Should he tell Jaymee that she was going to die? – a question to which there are no easy answers, no tried and tested formulas, only greater or lesser degrees of agony.

It is a dilemma every parent in this situation has to wrestle with. 'A children's doctor who is experienced will have a view of all the different perceptions that children of different ages, backgrounds and educational attainments might have about their own concept of mortality,' says Dr Simon Meller, one of the two specialists who looked after Jaymee at the Royal Marsden Hospital where she had her bone marrow transplant. 'If you're talking about children aged ten to thirteen, they can usually talk about the fact that cancer is a potentially fatal illness in quite a detached way. I think they hear what the doctor is saying, they know leukaemia kills children, but they believe they're immune from that. But children with cancer are usually very grown-up for their years and it may be that constant exposure to issues about cancer and death does speed up the process for children knowing about their own mortality.'

Almost every week, Dr Meller has to sit down with a family and tell them that their child is going to die. Often parents realize it before they're told because they have become so attuned to their child's condition, monitoring every blood test result, every change of drug. Children's cancer units encourage this. They believe in being as open and honest as possible because it makes parents feel involved in their child's treatment and does not give them false hope. It also means that if things start to go wrong, they can begin to prepare themselves for what lies ahead.

David could only make his decision on the basis of what he knew about Jaymee's personality. He decided she must not be told the truth. He believed she couldn't cope with it. He felt her mind was too logical and scientific. Most important, he said, she didn't believe in a life after death. He said the knowledge that she faced absolute extinction in a matter of weeks would make her last days 'a living hell'.

'I felt Jaymee couldn't take it. She'd be saying, "What happens after I'm dead, Daddy? Where am I going to be? What if I need you? How am I going to speak to you?"'

When I talked to Jaymee about this many months later, it became clear that she was more ambivalent about the issue than David had believed. 'It's a tough question,' she said. 'I don't really want to die, I don't want to die. But if I do I think there is an afterlife.'

At the time, though, the burden of deciding whether or not Jaymee should be told the truth fell on David's shoulders. Both he and his father instructed the doctors at Addenbrooke's that 'there must be no slip-ups. She must not be told.'

But the doctors disagreed with him. 'They felt that I should tell Jaymee,' David said. 'They felt that I should explain to her that she was going to die.'

Both David's parents supported his decision. 'The doctors felt Jaymee had a right to know that she was going to die so that she could enjoy her last days. We said she can enjoy her last days without knowing,' Rita said.

David had given the same instructions to Jaymee's headteacher on the day he went to tell him about her prognosis. Her classmates weren't to be told. Nobody was to say anything.

For David there was an even more important reason for keeping Jaymee in the dark. He didn't believe what the doctors were telling him. He thought they'd given up too soon. Dr Broadbent wasn't an expert in bone marrow transplantation, she was a specialist in children's cancer; and David wanted some more opinions before he accepted what she was saying.

'Instinctively I felt that they as doctors are human beings, and that Jaymee's war was not a war of skill waged by a doctor, it was a war waged by drugs and as such the world is a large place and new things happen all the time. And I felt that maybe Jaymee's doctors were not in a position to keep up to date with everything and perhaps some research laboratory somewhere may just have stumbled across something that could have helped. And I worked on that principle alone and off I went. I had six to eight weeks and during that time I could devote twenty-four hours of my day to Jaymee with the sole aim of finding out what was going on around the world.'

NHS doctors have their own description for a desperate search for medical opinions. They call it doctor-shopping. 'If you saw three independent experts about any particular disease and you got a consensus, that would be pretty remarkable inevitably,' said Simon Meller. 'If you doctor-shop you'll eventually find someone whose views will be outside the mainstream medical establishment, which may suit your ends as the patient or as the parent of the patient.'

This was what David was being told by Jaymee's original doctor at Addenbrooke's too. David's father had been with him during one of his discussions with Dr Broadbent. 'He was asking all the time about other options and he even said, "How about American doctors, would they be able to help?" And Dr Broadbent's remark was more or less that there are doctors in America who would do anything for money.'

Whatever term the NHS doctors were using, David didn't see it that way. From now on, all his efforts were to be concentrated on saving his daughter's life and he believed no one had the right to stop him.

'I couldn't accept that I shouldn't try. I wanted to be able to say to Jaymee, whether or not she's around, that I did everything I could do and I didn't take anybody else's word for the fact that she wasn't going to be here. That was very important to me.'

Above all, David Bowen simply refused to contemplate the possibility that Jaymee's illness could get the better of them both. 'I've never failed at anything in my entire life. I'm not capable of that, I don't see any purpose in it. It's a bit like wanting to win badly enough to be able to alter the odds in my favour. There's just a side of me that says that when I get launched into something there is no stopping me, no letting go, there is no other alternative. I will walk over anything and anyone to get to the point I wish to be at. I'll continue like a machine – I won't eat, I won't sleep. But I will achieve that task. That's the way I am.'

6

A Race Against Time

For the next six weeks David was true to his word. While Jaymee and Charlotte were in bed, he pored over every piece of medical literature he could get his hands on which related to second bone marrow transplants and Jaymee's particular type of leukaemia.

As far as he could see, a second transplant was the answer. After all, the original donor, Charlotte, was still available. Surely this was the solution. Jaymee's doctors didn't agree. In spite of David's insistence, her original doctors believed that the odds were firmly stacked against her.

Dr Broadbent told him that because the first transplant had failed after less than a year, the chances of another being successful were virtually non-existent. Not satisfied with this answer, David asked for a second opinion from the doctor who had performed Jaymee's first transplant, at the Royal Marsden Hospital in London.

Professor Ross Pinkerton is one of the country's leading experts in the treatment of acute myeloid leukaemia in children. A tall, bearded, softly spoken Irishman who is all too used to seeing children die from their disease, sometimes in agony, he says he is reluctant to perform treatments that have, in his view, no chance of a cure.

Professor Pinkerton told David it was not his policy to perform second transplants on children with relapsed leukaemia. 'In general, if the first transplant is successful, the

49

child will remain in remission for many years and in some cases be completely cured. Those who relapse tend to relapse within a couple of years of the transplant, and the problem with re-treating children after a bone marrow transplant is twofold. The first problem is that because they have had very intensive chemotherapy and in particular because the whole body has been given a high dose of radiation, then any other drugs that are given will inevitably have more serious side-effects, so it's that bit more difficult to get a response from further treatment.

'Secondly, the type of leukaemia she has, myeloid leukaemia, we know has to be given very high-dose treatment in order to clear the disease, and that's not feasible if it's attempted close to the transplant.'

Professor Pinkerton told David that although a second transplant was still technically possible because Charlotte was still around to donate her bone marrow, the risks would far outweigh the benefit to Jaymee. Not only would she have to spend several weeks, perhaps months, in hospital, but the likely side-effects of such intensive treatment would be severe. Because he believed there was no chance of curing Jaymee, he felt that putting her through another transplant simply wasn't justified.

Dr Simon Meller is a colleague of Ross Pinkerton's and was closely involved in the decision not to offer Jaymee another transplant. 'Anyone would think that the Child B case was the first time doctors have ever had to face these decisions. They're facing them constantly in children's cancer work. They're constantly reaching a point in a child's treatment which may be the first or second relapse of the disease where the doctors are as certain as they ever can be that they're beyond the possibility of a cure. If you can buy six months of good-quality life for a child, then that in my mind is about the break-even point and it depends on what the child has to go through to get it.'

Ross Pinkerton puts it even more bluntly: 'At the end of the day, it's the interest of the child which is paramount. We're not going to be right all the time, but the decisions that we take and the advice that we give is based on the primary goal, which is not to harm the child simply because we all find it so difficult to let go.'

David admits that he was driven partly by the realization that he could not bear to see Jaymee die. 'People have told me it would make me stronger. I couldn't see it myself. People said that I would get over it. Couldn't see it myself. I felt that I would not be able to cope.'

So to David, keeping Jaymee alive – 'saving me', as Jaymee puts it – became a challenge. He simply refused to accept what the NHS doctors were saying. He believed he knew his daughter better than anyone else and he had seen how well she had responded to the vast amounts of toxic drugs she'd been given over the last five years. If she had done it before, she could do it again.

Despite Dr Broadbent's warnings about American doctors being willing to do anything for money, David was determined to seek out medical opinion there, particularly as his brother, Graham, lived in California and could get access to information for him.

'My father telephoned me at work and told me the news about Jaymee,' Graham said. 'He asked if anything could be done from the American side.' In America, the telephone is usually the first source of information, so Graham consulted the phone book for listings under cancer and discovered the National Cancer Institute Information Service and a freephone number.

'You give them all the details you have about the particular patient or problem and they tell you where to go for help,' Graham said. They told him about an organization called PDQ which runs a large database giving up-to-date information on cancer treatment and listings of every clinical trial taking place in America. The database can be accessed through the Internet too and is aimed directly at patients and their families.

'You can use PDQ to learn more about current treatments for your child's kind of cancer,' it says. 'Bring this material with you when you see your child's doctor. You can talk with the doctor, who knows your child and has the facts about your child's disease, about which treatment would be best.' It was all very consumer-oriented and deliberately intended to help patients and their families ask questions.

Graham telephoned PDQ immediately and told them about Jaymee, giving them as much information as he could about her condition and the treatment she had already had. In return, they faxed him information about the relevant clinical trials and gave him the names of doctors who might be able to help.

Then he simply rang them up. The first was a Dr Paul Zeltzer, a children's cancer expert at one of Los Angeles's main teaching hospitals. 'It was easy to get through to him and we spoke on three occasions,' Graham said. 'He wanted to know as much as possible about Jaymee, and by this stage David had managed to get some of her medical notes. Dr Zeltzer seemed confident. To him it was almost routine that there were more treatment options available for Jaymee. He didn't rule anything out.'

David and Graham had wasted no time. By 24 January, four days after David's discussion with Dr Broadbent, Ross Pinkerton had sent Dr Zeltzer a fax containing details of Jaymee's treatment. Again, Professor Pinkerton emphasized in this fax: 'I would be rather in favour of palliative therapy as I do not think there is any realistic curable option.'

Through a contact at another large children's hospital in

the area, Graham had been given the name of another doctor. His name was Mitchell Cairo and Dr Zeltzer agreed that he would probably be the person most likely to help Jaymee. Dr Cairo was in charge of the transplant programme at the hospital and already knew Ross Pinkerton from the international bone marrow circuit. By now, David had demanded copies of all Jaymee's medical notes from Addenbrooke's and he sent two large files to Dr Cairo by Federal Express. Now the Americans had everything they needed to make an assessment of Jaymee – except the patient herself.

'I felt Jaymee's own doctors were letting her down,' David said. 'We were in contact with doctors who cost thousands of dollars, doctors we didn't know who gave us their home numbers, their car phone numbers, their bleeper numbers.' A few days later, Dr Cairo had a telephone conversation with David. His assessment of Jaymee's chances of surviving another bone marrow transplant was much more optimistic than that of her two NHS doctors. He told David that there was about a 60 per cent chance of her surviving a second transplant, and a 30 per cent chance of her leukaemia still being in remission after two years.

'That night,' said Rita, 'we got some sleep.'

But there had been no discussion of the numbers or precise medical conditions of the patients to whom Dr Cairo had given second transplants, nor of how successful they had been. Dr Cairo had simply said he would be prepared to do it. But David was right about the 'thousands of dollars': the bill would be more than $250,000. As Dr Broadbent had suggested to him, American medicine does not come cheap. Because of the amount of time David had spent with Jaymee over the last few years, he had put his career on hold and relied on short-term contracts for his income, so he was in no position to pay for her treatment himself.

Nevertheless, he believed that if the Americans were

prepared to offer Jaymee a second transplant, then her NHS doctors at the Royal Marsden could do it too. 'I'd asked the American doctors to design me a regime for Jaymee that they could pass on to her NHS doctors because I thought obviously the Americans must know something they didn't know,' he said.

But when David went to see Dr Simon Meller at the Marsden, armed with his information from America, the response was sceptical. 'Mr Bowen wanted to know why, if Mitchell Cairo, who is a respected second opinion, said it could be done, we wouldn't do it at the Marsden,' Dr Meller said. The answer was that he thought the American was being wildly over-optimistic about Jaymee's chances.

'My feeling was that Cairo's opinion was based on entirely inadequate numbers. He didn't say, "I have done twenty cases like this" – it was not precise information. And the reason it wasn't precise information was because it doesn't exist. I don't think anyone who has looked at Jaymee's case has given such an optimistic view. My line was that if Mitchell Cairo felt the chances were that good and if in his institution he was studying this particular approach then Jaymee should go to him. He shouldn't be telling another institution to do a one-off experiment that they weren't happy with.'

The statistics Dr Meller had consulted showed that no one in Jaymee's condition who had relapsed within less than a year of a first transplant had survived for longer after a second one and he told David that the Marsden would not be prepared to offer Jaymee the treatment.

'In the 1980s we did a series of three or four second transplants and without exception the children had a shorter duration of life after their second transplant than after their first,' Dr Meller told me. 'So if the duration of survival after the transplant is almost always less than the first and it's going to be a stormy road, then nearly always you're not going to create any useful good-quality life for the child. My own personal view is that for leukaemia it's not a good strategy, because it's going to save very few lives and I know for certain that a second transplant is never as easy as the first.

'We explained all that to David Bowen. He still wanted a second transplant. He took the attitude that even if doctors were saying there was only a 1 per cent chance of success, unless he was convinced himself by taking opinions from many doctors that there was a zero chance of success, he wanted Jaymee to have a second transplant.'

David says all he could do at that point was to second-guess what Jaymee herself would have wanted. 'I felt that Jaymee would have made the same decision and that was most important to me. I know I would have taken the chance. I would have taken a 1 per cent chance, but that's my own personal view. I had to think about it from her viewpoint and think about how she was going to react taking into account all her past performance. I wasn't playing God. I was genuinely doing the best for her which I think any parent would choose to do.'

Dr Broadbent at Addenbrooke's also refused to be swayed by the Americans' view. At this point relations between David and the doctor who had been in charge of Jaymee's treatment for the last five years began to break down. Dr Broadbent has never discussed Jaymee's case publicly, but according to David, 'She felt that I would better serve my time by going home and spending more time with my daughter, that I wasn't doing her any favours and that I obviously didn't have her best interests at heart.'

But for Jaymee's doctors, there was an ethos at stake as well as the life of an individual child, an ethos which had been acquired through years of working in the NHS. 'I don't think any doctor should be forced to do a treatment which he or she feels unhappy in delivering,' said Simon Meller. 'That's the bottom line and I don't think they should be forced to do it if the consensus view of his or her peers is that the decision is reasonable, and at that point I can see that a dissatisfied family or patient might go elsewhere.'

But as each day passed and the arguments continued, it was obvious to all those around her that Jaymee's condition was getting steadily worse. The leukaemia was literally invading her body. 'I'd get very high temperatures and I'd just start shaking very badly. I'd get stitches from shaking so bad. Once my temperature had gone down, it would take about half an hour to warm me back up again. I'd be there with at least three duvets all wrapped round me and I'd still be cold. I'd sit on the sofa all day with the three duvets on me, then as I'd start to warm up I'd take them off one at a time.' Her appetite was beginning to vanish too. 'I wouldn't be eating very much,' she said. 'You imagine a whole pie cut into quarters, I couldn't even eat a whole quarter.' She had no idea that as each day passed, she was running out of time. She is also adamant that she did not know that her leukaemia had come back. 'No one told me what was going on. I thought maybe I'd just come down with some sort of flu, some sort of bug. I'd had a blood test and I'd got something wrong with my blood.'

Every other day, Jaymee went back to the Royal Marsden Hospital for a blood transfusion to keep her symptoms under control. By now, David, Charlotte and Jaymee had moved into Rita and Ossie's house so that they could be near the hospital. Rita watched in despair as Jaymee's life seemed to be ebbing away. 'We saw it in front of our own eyes, we saw her going down. She couldn't move around. She had a low quality of life which was something that stuck out in my mind, because when the doctors kept talking about her last days and the quality of her life and that we should make it happy, I knew that they were talking a lot of nonsense because the quality of life she had then was nothing. Nothing. She was really beginning to suffer.'

'She looked like she was dying and as a parent I couldn't tell her she was dying,' David said. 'We knew that if she died she would just pass away in her sleep. It would be very painless. She'd just close her eyes and wouldn't wake up.'

At night, when Jaymee was in bed, David went on trying to get information from America. He hardly slept. And however much he had tried to convince himself that if Jaymee was going to die it would be better if she did so while she was asleep, he hated it when she *was* sleeping because he was terrified she would never wake up. Rita had put Jaymee into a small bedroom on her own, leaving Charlotte and her two cousins, Rochelle and Nadine, sharing a room together. The two girls often stayed with Rita. Her house was like a second home to them. Giving Jaymee a room of her own was deliberate. If she died, Rita didn't want it to happen in a room with the other children.

Ossie bought a baby alarm so that David could monitor Jaymee's breathing when he was trying to sleep downstairs. He would put the transmitter close to Jaymee's mouth, and the receiver next to David's ear. But no one slept very much during those weeks. While the children remained blissfully unaware of the truth, the adults in the Bowen family were becoming increasingly desperate.

'Sometimes all three of us would end up in Jaymee's room together,' Rita said. 'Sometimes Ossie would come, he would say Jaymee is coughing, but by the time I'm getting up to go in, David is running up the stairs as well. And we're all in there. You couldn't sleep when she was getting worse because you didn't know what was going to happen.'

One night, Rita got out of bed to check that Jaymee was all

right. 'I put my hand on her and she was cold, cold, cold. I stood there and I started to shake and I'm scared. I don't know what I thought. That was the biggest fright of my life with her and I'm thinking how do I try and turn her to see if she's alive. That's all I wanted to know, if she was alive, because her skin was very cold and they say when people die, they get cold. I'm standing there shaking and I'm trying to pull the sheet to put it over her and David came up and I said, "I'm just trying to see if she's all right and I'm frightened to wake her up." He just pushed her and she sort of stirred. I nearly fell down. I just said, thank God for that. I didn't go back to sleep. I mean, after something like that, you can't sleep. You think if I'd gone in there and found her dead, what would I have done? And you just don't want it to happen to you.'

Both David's parents supported his decision to try and get more treatment for Jaymee. But they were also thinking ahead. Without telling David they began making arrangements for Jaymee's funeral.

'It was just that if we got to that stage we would be ready to act,' Rita said. 'We even had her favourite songs that she liked. We'd got it all written down and we thought of some children's hymns and then I got in touch with the vicar.'

'Positive thinking is extremely important to David,' his father said. 'As far as he's concerned, he just won't entertain any negative thoughts about her. She is going to be all right and that's that.'

But Rita could see that underneath his optimism and determination to succeed, her son was afraid. 'When Jaymee was ill he said, I'm coming down to your house and I'm coming to stay because if she's going to die I want her to die at your house. We thought he wasn't going to be able to handle her alone and he knew that if he was with us it would be handled for him and that's what he was looking for.'

Last November, ten months after Jaymee's doctors had delivered their bombshell, David reflected on his decision to challenge their assumptions. One afternoon we were sitting talking in a coffee shop, and he made what I thought was a surprising admission. 'It was cowardice that made me fight for Jaymee,' he said. 'I kept thinking of her lying in a coffin and I just wasn't ready to face that.'

What parent ever can?

'It's often very hard for the family to accept it,' says Ross Pinkerton. 'It often takes many days or many weeks for them to come to terms with it and we encourage second opinions. We encourage them to go and talk to other parents and families who've been in a similar situation to try and come to terms with the position.'

But David wasn't interested in coming to terms with the idea of Jaymee's death. He was offered counselling but he refused. To him, giving in was not on the agenda until every possible avenue of inquiry had been exhausted. 'They're very good at trying to prepare you,' he said. 'The system will help you with anything to do with preparing yourself for the death of a child but won't help you if you want to try and avoid that.'

David had promised himself that he would spend every available moment of his time trying to find an alternative solution for Jaymee, but there was another problem which demanded his attention. By now, Alyson had learned that Jaymee was only expected to last another few weeks and she wanted to see her.

It was an extraordinarily difficult dilemma for them all. Jaymee and Charlotte had had practically no contact with their mother for years, so there were few if any emotional ties. David believed that if these were to be the last weeks of

Jaymee's life, they should be spent as peacefully as possible rather than immersing her in what was bound to be more emotional turmoil. Yet Alyson was her mother, and what mother wouldn't wish to see her child before that child died? Eventually it was agreed that Alyson could see Jaymee and Charlotte, and over the next few weeks they met on several occasions.

By the second week in February it was clear that, despite the optimism expressed by the American doctors, neither of Jaymee's original NHS consultants was willing to consider offering her a second bone marrow transplant. But there was one more avenue to pursue and, after days of correspondence with the Americans, it turned out to be a British one. During one of his many phone calls to the States, David was given the name of a leukaemia specialist based at a London teaching hospital who might be able to help. His name was Professor John Goldman.

Professor Goldman is the head of leukaemia research at the Hammersmith Hospital, and is one of the country's most eminent leukaemia specialists, dealing mainly with adults and renowned for taking on difficult cases. As time was running out, David didn't wait to be referred through the proper channels. He telephoned Professor Goldman's secretary direct and made an appointment. On 13 February, three weeks after David had been told that Jaymee had no more than two months to live, the Bowen family saw Professor Goldman in his outpatient clinic at the Hammersmith Hospital. After examining Jaymee, he gave his verdict. What he told the Bowens gave them all cause for hope.

'The thing I remembered most about him is that he said that if a family is fighting this hard, they should get better than palliative care. Words to that effect,' Ossie told me. 'He spoke to all of us and then he asked Jaymee to go out and said,

"I'll have a word with Daddy now." He said yes, we can do a second bone marrow transplant but we don't like doing it under a year after the first one. Jaymee was getting pretty close to a year and he was considering the options and more or less said that he would be prepared to do it.'

John Goldman is a formidable intellectual whose belief is that no policy should be set in stone and every avenue should be explored before reaching a decision to stop giving a patient aggressive treatment. 'We are doctors, not robots,' he told me. 'To say a treatment is not in a child's best interests is very dogmatic.' He remembers the meeting with the Bowens well. 'When I told David Bowen that there was a good case for giving Jaymee further treatment, his face lit up.'

Professor Goldman said that in his opinion, Jaymee could withstand more chemotherapy in the hope of getting her leukaemia into remission. If it worked, then a second bone marrow transplant would be feasible. 'It's not appropriate to refuse treatment. You should always keep your options open and try and work out a compromise,' he said.

This was precisely what David thought too. He believed he was being stonewalled by Jaymee's original doctors and that was partly what persuaded him to look for alternatives. 'To accept totally what a doctor tells you, you must assume that their thought process is perfect, that they've taken into consideration every single available piece of information all around the world. The decision to challenge them was based on doctors who said Jaymee had a better chance than her original doctors were giving her.'

Nevertheless, Professor Goldman's assessment of Jaymee's chance of long-term survival after a second transplant was nowhere near as optimistic as the Americans'. He thought her chances were about 10 per cent but, like David, he believed 10 per cent was better than nothing. However, because he knew the chance of success was slim, Professor Goldman accepted that giving Jaymee another transplant would be tantamount to experimentation.

It was a risk he was prepared to take. 'I think the word experimental means different things to different people,' he said. 'To me it means something where the chance of success is not very great but you could be rewarded with a magnificent result if you're lucky. There are others to whom experimental means not to be undertaken. That's not me.'

As a specialist in adults' leukaemia, Professor Goldman took a very different view from Jaymee's original NHS doctors, both of whom believe there should be more stringent ethical restrictions applied to high-risk experimental treatment for children than for adults who are able to give informed consent to such treatment.

'Children's cancer specialists get quite a hard time from adult specialists, and we're very often accused of being too protective towards our patients and too much aware of inflicting pain and distress because somehow they feel we should make children put up with more in order to get better,' said Simon Meller.

'I think,' he went on, 'it's arrogant for adult specialists to accuse paediatricians who've worked in the field for twenty years or more and are very experienced, of not doing it right for children – in other words, implying that the treatment should be given regardless of the physical and emotional costs. Children's specialists would always see it differently. They'd always see that the total interests of the child are their first concern, not a cure at all costs.'

But at that moment, David wasn't interested in ethical debates. His mind was focused on one thing: keeping Jaymee alive. After their meeting, Professor Goldman wrote immediately to Professor Pinkerton and to Dr Broadbent in Cambridge to tell them what he thought. Even if there was a bed available for Jaymee at the Hammersmith, David couldn't simply bypass the administrative procedures of the NHS. Jaymee would have to be referred to Professor Goldman formally by one of her original doctors. David asked Dr Broadbent in Cambridge if she would fax a letter to Goldman authorizing what is known as a tertiary referral.

By now Dr Broadbent had had enough. Two days later she wrote to Professor Goldman. 'Mr David Bowen has demanded that I fax a tertiary referral to you after reportedly discussing with you a second bone marrow transplant for his daughter Jaymee. I have already referred Jaymee back to Dr Pinkerton at the Royal Marsden Hospital for a second opinion and he agrees with my judgement that a second transplant is not indicated in this case . . . I am sure you are also aware that he has sought opinions from a variety of other transplant experts around the world.' Dr Broadbent told Professor Goldman: 'I am afraid it is against my medical judgement that a second transplant is indicated and I would therefore have difficulty in recommending this within the NHS.'

There was one more port of call for David and it took him right to the heart of decision-making in the National Health Service. He approached his local health authority in Cambridge and asked if they would authorize treatment for Jaymee at the Hammersmith. Had they agreed, the health authority would have had to pay for the treatment too because the health authority had no formal contract with the Hammersmith even though it is an NHS hospital. It would have been, in NHS jargon, an extra-contractual referral.

The man at Cambridge Health Authority who took most responsibility for deciding whether to fund Jaymee's treatment was Dr Ron Zimmern, the Director of Public Health. It was his job to talk not only to Jaymee's original doctors but also to Professor Goldman. The question Dr Zimmern needed to answer to determine whether it was worth spending NHS money on Jaymee's treatment was whether it would be 'clinically effective'. It wasn't a matter of whether NHS money should be used to pay for private medical care – that was allowed in the reformed NHS – but whether spending that money would be an efficient use of public funds.

Again, Jaymee's original doctors repeated their view that another transplant would not be in Jaymee's best interests. Simon Meller remembers his conversation with Dr Zimmern well. 'He wanted confirmation that the Royal Marsden wasn't planning to do a second transplant and he wanted to know if a second transplant in this situation should be regarded as a standard treatment, to which I replied that it was definitely an experimental procedure. Then he wanted confirmation that we weren't running an experimental study of this nature for children and I said that we weren't. He also wanted to know whether it was likely that any other NHS children's leukaemia unit would have a programme of this sort if the Marsden didn't, but I said I thought it very unlikely.'

When Ron Zimmern spoke to Professor Goldman he acknowledged that such treatment would have to be classified as experimental but that he believed it was worth a try. Dr Zimmern weighed up the medical advice and made his decision. No, treating Jaymee would not in his opinion be clinically effective.

There was another important issue involved too. As far as the Health Authority was concerned, David Bowen had already flouted the rules by organizing what they described as a 'self-referral' to Professor Goldman. He had already had his second opinion from the Royal Marsden. Now he wanted them to pay for treatment which Jaymee's own doctors refused to recommend. They were not prepared to sanction the behaviour of this father who went to see doctors without a formal referral from the NHS and then expected them to pay the bill. They refused David's request.

No formal meetings ever took place between David Bowen and the two people at the Health Authority on whose shoulders the decision about whether to fund Jaymee's treatment lay. But over the next fortnight a series of faxes and letters flew back and forth between the Bowen camp and the Health Authority headquarters on the outskirts of Cambridge. They exposed the medical dilemmas at the heart of Jaymee's case and the checks and balances on NHS spending which now lay in the hands of health authority managers.

As far as David was concerned, all that mattered was that he had found a doctor willing to treat his daughter and the Health Authority was refusing to pay the bill.

He faxed Dr Zimmern: 'I am writing to you to ask for your explanation of what you mean by "not clinically effective". My recent experience has been that of delaying tactics. As I am sure you know, Jaymee's consultant at Addenbrooke's said she has a matter of days (possibly weeks) to live and therefore time is extremely important in this particular case . . . I can assure you that I will seek every avenue open to me in order to preserve my daughter's life.'

But the fax he received in reply from Dr Zimmern the next day said simply: 'I regret that I have a policy of not speaking or corresponding directly with patients or their relatives about extra-contractual referrals.'

David was furious and immediately fired off another fax to Cambridge asking Dr Zimmern if it was his personal policy or that of the Health Authority which dictated his stance of not speaking directly to patients or their families. Unable to understand the authority's reasoning, David also asked Dr Zimmern if money was the problem.

Later the same day, Zimmern faxed again: 'I understand totally your concerns and the sense of distress which you must feel. Should there be any misunderstanding I should state quite clearly that any decision taken by the Commission will be made taking all clinical and other relevant matters into consideration and not on financial grounds.'

By now, David was starting to get angry. 'I had put forward what I felt was a sensible case that had good merits, and the fact that they dismissed it upset me, but the fact that they dismissed it without involving me or Jaymee made me feel that perhaps their opinion wasn't a valid one.'

But Stephen Thornton, the man in charge of Cambridge Health Authority and the person with whom Ron Zimmern had discussed his reasons for refusing to pay for Jaymee's treatment, understood only too well the agonizing nature of the decision they had taken. 'In all of these cases, there's never an absolute right answer because we're talking about value judgements, about shades of grey, not absolute black and white,' Mr Thornton said. 'We always have to remember that we're talking about real people's lives and illness and that makes it extremely difficult. In this case we came to the conclusion that the treatment we were being asked to fund would not be effective. In other words, it wouldn't work, and also that it would be the wrong thing for Jaymee to have at her particular stage of illness – that quite frankly it would probably do her more harm than good.'

But time was slipping away. If Dr Broadbent's calculations were correct, Jaymee had no more than four weeks left to live. 'Things were beginning to get fairly desperate,' David said. Jaymee was now too ill to realize what was happening.

Again, David turned to Professor Goldman for help. By now it was clear to everyone that time was running out. Even if the Health Authority had been willing to pay, there was now no bed available for Jaymee at the Hammersmith, so Professor Goldman did the only thing he could think of. He gave David the name of a colleague of his, a private doctor in Harley Street. His name was Peter Gravett.

Dr Gravett had done his medical training in the army and spent much of his career as a doctor overseas. After retiring from army medical practice, he set up a full-time private specialist bone marrow transplant service in London and had earned the respect of many NHS doctors.

'Peter Gravett is an exception, a real exception in that he's working privately and pretty much on his own, but with the respect of his colleagues in the NHS,' said Simon Meller. 'He's set up an outstandingly good transplant service. There is no one else in London apart from him who would have been able to take on such a case in the private sector. He is not in any sense a maverick and is in no sense practising outside the establishment or undertaking inappropriate treatments or research experiments.'

It was 20 February by the time Jaymee saw Peter Gravett. Just before midday, David, Ossie, Jaymee and Charlotte found themselves in a hospital waiting room. This time it was the rather elegant, thickly carpeted and expensively furnished London Clinic near Regent's Park, a far cry from the well-worn linoleum-covered corridors of the Hammersmith Hospital. This is where Peter Gravett does most of his work and it was here that he first met Jaymee. He had already discussed her case with Professor Goldman on the telephone and had talked to David. The consultation he gave the family that day was free. He wanted to examine Jaymee and had been sent her most recent blood test results from the Royal Marsden.

'I wasn't at all convinced about the arguments that she'd had enough and didn't want any more treatment,' Dr Gravett said. 'From the conversations that I had with her I thought that she was perfectly prepared to go on, even though she had spent a lot of time in hospital.'

He told David that, like John Goldman, he would be willing to give her more chemotherapy, and if that succeeded in getting rid of most of the leukaemia, he would be prepared to consider another bone marrow transplant. He proposed to treat Jaymee at the private Portland Hospital for Women and Children round the corner from the London Clinic. There would be a bed available almost immediately. Although he had reservations about the wisdom of another bone marrow transplant, Peter Gravett thought it was at least worthwhile trying to get Jaymee into remission.

'My problem,' Gravett later told me, 'was having her there in front of me and simply having to do the best for her that I could. There are occasions when the best thing is simply to recommend that active treatment just isn't indicated. But I didn't think that was the case with Jaymee because there were some options that hadn't been explored at the time.'

Dr Gravett wrote to David, formally agreeing to take Jaymee on and confirming that the cost of the treatment would be £75,000. David firmly believed the NHS should pay the bill, so he contacted Cambridge Health Authority again.

Six days later Dr Zimmern wrote to Peter Gravett. 'Given your assessment, together with the advice that I received from Jaymee's medical advisers at both Addenbrooke's and the Marsden and in view of Department of Health guidance on the funding of treatment not of a proven nature, I regret that my Commission is unwilling to fund this treatment.'

To David, this was the final blow. 'I was taking hours and hours and hours out of my day fighting the Health Authority and putting forward a rational case and listening to doctors saying Jaymee had a chance and then the Health Authority blow it apart with one letter. I was gutted and very very angry. It's not like buying a house and your not exchanging contracts on the day. This was life and death. The consequences of failure were death.'

To Professor Goldman, who believed that paying for Jaymee's treatment would not be a waste of NHS money, the decision was 'unduly definite and dogmatic. In some countries, particularly the United States, the decision that Cambridge Health Authority made would have been regarded as extremely old-fashioned and out of date. I think almost every leukaemia specialist there would have certainly recommended further treatment with anti-leukaemia drugs for Jaymee, and the idea of a second transplant would have been contemplated for this year or the beginning of next year. I think the Health Authority believed they were acting in Jaymee's best interests, but what really are her best interests is a matter for debate.'

'I was out of options,' David said. 'Time was at its limit. I'd been told that Jaymee had six to eight weeks and I knew that if Jaymee was Jaymee she'd hang on for the eight weeks. If it was you or I, perhaps we'd die in four weeks, but Jaymee would hang on. I wouldn't wish what I went through on anyone. It wasn't that there was nothing the Health Authority could do, it was that they wouldn't do it. They were sentencing my daughter to die. She'd committed no crime and they could have given her a chance. Money cannot buy life but it can buy extensions and I honestly, wholeheartedly believed that if they gave her that chance she'd make it.'

David decided there was only one more avenue open to him. 'He said, "I'm going to take this to court,"' Ossie recalls. 'So I said, "OK."'

7

The Making of Child B

When David took Cambridge Health Authority to court, the private struggle and personal grief of the Bowen family became public property on a scale they could never have imagined. While the right of a ten-year-old girl – known only as Child B – to receive potentially life-saving treatment on the National Health Service was being decided by the might of the law, that life was fast running out. On the day judgement was pronounced, Jaymee was in hospital having a blood transfusion to keep her alive a little longer.

'I didn't really have time to sit in court,' David said. 'The worst thing that could have happened to me would have been that Jaymee died while I was physically in court when I should have been spending my time with her.'

But for the man for whom failure was not an option, there was no other choice. To David, it was simple. He had found two British doctors who believed it was worthwhile giving his daughter more treatment and the NHS was refusing to pay the bill because it said the chance of success was so small. If they didn't pay, Jaymee would be dead within a matter of weeks, even days. What right did they have to refuse?

In a formal statement sworn to the court David said: 'As every day passes, the chances of treatment being successful decrease. I believe Jaymee is rushing towards a precipice. If she were an adult she would be able to make a choice herself as to whether or not she had a second bone marrow transplant. I believe that she should be entitled to that chance of life.'

Because she was a minor, it was Jaymee who was granted legal aid to fund the case, with her father, acting as what is known as her 'next friend', taking the case to court on her behalf.

Having got legal aid, David's lawyers had to convince a judge that it was a case worth hearing at all. On Monday 6 March 1995, they found themselves before Mr Justice Laws, explaining why they wanted to challenge the Health Authority's decision to refuse payment for Jaymee's treatment.

The judge was absolutely certain of one thing: if they challenged the Health Authority on the basis of whether their decision was right or wrong, the case would fail because the courts couldn't intervene in clinical decisions or the way in which public funds were allocated. They could only judge whether the decision had been reached in a lawful manner. Having acted on many occasions as a barrister representing the Treasury, Mr Justice Laws knew exactly what the legal parameters were as far as challenging the way in which public money was spent.

They must fight the case on the grounds of Jaymee's right to life, he said. It was a right not yet enshrined in English law, but was part of the European Convention on Human Rights. If they did that, he believed there would be a case for the Health Authority to answer.

'We all knew we could fail because we knew we couldn't make the Health Authority pay,' David said. 'The best we could hope for was that they would be ordered to go away and reconsider, but we knew we had no other choice and everybody pitched in. They all had other important work to do, but it had to be pushed to one side because Jaymee's case was all-consuming. Her time was limited. Everyone had to work hard just to get the case to court.'

It was to last two days, beginning on Thursday 9 March, with judgement the following day. On the Wednesday afternoon, David met Rose Sunter, a solicitor from Sharpe Pritchard, the firm of London lawyers who had been helping to prepare the groundwork for the case.

Rose Sunter is used to dealing with the complexities of child abuse cases and other areas affecting children's rights, but she says that for her the case of the 'Crown versus Cambridge Health Authority ex parte "B"' was completely different from anything she had dealt with before. 'I've done cases where I've come out of court and parents have attacked me and I've had to be taken off by the police down back entrances,' she said. 'I had one case in the High Court where the man involved followed me out, beating me with a stick whenever he could get near me; but in terms of sheer emotion, Jaymee's case was more devastating. Usually I act for a local authority, and however awful it is you're one step removed. Here I was acting for the father and he was relying on me.'

Her first impression of David Bowen was how young he was. None of her colleagues could believe he was old enough to have a ten-year-old daughter. Since the court case, Rose has come to know the Bowens extremely well and is now a close friend. Recalling that first meeting with David, she says it was difficult to appreciate quite how ill Jaymee was at that point. 'David told me she was going to the Royal Marsden Hospital every other day for blood transfusions and platelets, but if you haven't any experience of what that is like, you don't really know what it means. He told me Jaymee was virtually confined to bed at home and wasn't doing anything but watching television and sleeping. Quite a lot later, I realized what they had actually been going through and how awful it was.'

At that meeting, Rose says David seemed to be very much in control and very positive about the court case ahead. This

is the side of David Bowen most people know. It is his optimism and belief in his own ability to overcome obstacles
which would defeat most people that drive him on.

But that afternoon he revealed a crack in his armour. Away
from his family where he maintained strict control of his
emotions at all times, he snapped. 'He started crying,' Rose
said. 'It's strange to see a man cry and he cried very openly, he
didn't feel embarrassed or upset about it, it just happened.'

The next morning, Rose met David and his father outside the
Law Courts in the Strand, an imposing Victorian gothic
building with endless staircases, corridors, back entrances
and courtrooms – a place where the most complex and far-
reaching legal cases in the land are heard and judged, and
where fates are decreed by a process which seems daunting
and far removed from the reality of everyday life.

But it was a process which David believed would favour his
daughter. 'He had all Jaymee's medical records with him in
two massive lever-arch files which he carried around in Ice-
land carrier bags,' Rose said. 'He seemed to take them everywhere with him, so he had his briefcase, his files and his
mobile phone. I didn't realize until afterwards that he was
rather expecting the judge to take these medical files and read
the notes, and make his own clinical decision, which of course
wasn't what it was about.'

David knew this was his last chance and he wanted the rest
of the legal team to know it too. Before the court case began
he showed them all a photograph of Jaymee. 'I said, look,
she can't be here herself but this is who you are fighting for.
She's my daughter, she's alive, and this is her when she was
healthy and we can keep her here if we fight. Of all the things
you've ever done in your entire life, to save a human life is
probably the greatest accolade you could ever have.'

On that first day, before the media had come to hear about

the case, the lawyers argued statistics. What chance of success would there be if Jaymee had a second bone marrow transplant? Was it 30 per cent, 20 per cent, 10 per cent or much less, as little as 1 or 2 per cent? The judge had seen the evidence from the American doctors, from Professor Goldman at the Hammersmith, from Peter Gravett at the London Clinic and from Jaymee's original NHS specialists, Valerie Broadbent at Addenbrooke's and Professor Pinkerton at the Royal Marsden. Essentially they divided into two camps – Professor Goldman and Peter Gravett on one side and Professor Pinkerton and Valerie Broadbent on the other. The consensus of opinion seemed to be that the Americans' assessment of Jaymee's chances was over-optimistic.

Throughout the day, David listened to the arguments put forward by his lawyers and by those representing Cambridge Health Authority. He made copious notes. But never for a moment did he forget that what all the learned lawyers were talking about was his daughter and that her time was running out. In front of him, propped up on the desk, was the photograph of Jaymee he had shown his legal team. It was a school photograph taken the summer before her leukaemia relapsed and he took it everywhere with him. Her dark curly hair was restored to shoulder length after the onslaught of all the chemotherapy she'd been given, and her huge brown eyes gazed confidently at him. He says it was his belief in her that had got him this far.

'At the end of the day, I hope that if Jaymee passes on, she can, from wherever she is, look down and say my father did the best for me. And if she can say that, then I've played my part.'

By Thursday lunchtime, David's barrister had finished putting his side of the argument. Now it was the Health Authority's turn. Only their lawyers were in court. Neither Stephen Thornton nor Ron Zimmern, the two men who had made the decision not to fund Jaymee's treatment, was there. They believed it was up to their legal team to argue their case for them while they got on with the business of running the Health Authority. 'We didn't think it would be a high-profile case beforehand,' said Mr Thornton. 'We hadn't the slightest inkling that it was going to be the health story of the year.' Before the case began, the Health Authority's solicitor came over and introduced himself to David and Ossie and made it clear that he was all too aware that David would rather be with Jaymee than in court.

As far as the Health Authority was concerned, what was important was to explain to the court the process by which they'd arrived at their decision not to fund Jaymee's treatment. They believed it wasn't so much the decision itself which mattered, but rather that the Health Authority could hold its head up and prove it had been made in a legitimate way.

To David, of course, it seemed perfectly clear that there was a right and a wrong answer. Right meant giving Jaymee another chance of life, wrong meant allowing her to die.

'It was frightening,' he said. 'There was the defence saying it was effectively in Jaymee's best interests to die, and there was I thinking to myself, How the hell can you tell me that it's in my daughter's best interests to die? And I was thinking, Come on someone, say something before I do. Luckily Mr Justice Laws would stand up and ask the Health Authority's barrister what could be more important than the life of a ten-year-old child?'

But if the Health Authority was refusing to pay for Jaymee's treatment on the grounds that it wasn't clinically effective, where should the line be drawn between judgements made by doctors and the wishes of patients and their parents?

Underlying everything that was being argued in court, this was the crucial question, and it was one Mr Justice Laws was anxious to get to grips with that first day. To help him, he used the analogy of the legendary Spanish warrior El Cid. 'El Cid had had to decide whether to take an arrow out of his chest before riding on to the battlefield,' Rose said. 'The judge argued that telling him he might live if he removed the arrow, but would die if he didn't, was a clinical judgement, but the decision to go on to the battlefield without having the arrow removed was not.

'The judge said that it was the doctors' duty to say, "Here are the options and the possible outcomes and here's our recommendation," but the actual decision couldn't be a clinical one – it should be up to the parents or patient to decide, and he said that this was the equivalent of El Cid deciding to ride on to the battlefield. Of course, David loved that.'

'When Justice Laws mentioned El Cid I knew in my heart of hearts that he was on Jaymee's side. He knew what he was doing, so that was a very good moment for me,' said David.

But the Health Authority raised another issue in court that Thursday afternoon, which took him completely by surprise. Suddenly their barrister was talking about money, something Dr Zimmern had told him had nothing to do with the decision about whether to pay for Jaymee's treatment. David had the fax from Dr Zimmern which he'd been sent on 21 February. It said: 'Should there be any misunderstanding I should state quite clearly that any decision taken by the Commission will be made taking all clinical and other relevant matters into consideration and not on financial grounds.'

Yet in his official written evidence, sworn before the court two weeks later, Dr Zimmern said: 'I also considered that the substantial expenditure on treatment with such small prospect of success would not be an effective use of resources. The amount of funds available for health care are not limitless.'

It was a contradiction the judge was quick to point out.

'The father might be forgiven for reflecting that it amounted to something of a volte-face,' he said.

David couldn't believe what he was hearing. 'In all their faxes they'd confirmed it wasn't money,' he said.

'He was very, very angry when he discovered that money had come into it,' Rose said. 'He felt he'd been cheated, that if he'd been told the problem was money in the middle of January he could have gone out and raised it, there were things he could have sold. He felt they'd deliberately taken from him the opportunity to earn that money.'

It was obvious that David Bowen would have the moral high ground to himself in this case, but as far as Stephen Thornton, the chief executive of Cambridge Health Authority, was concerned, there were other equally important issues involved. He had a daughter the same age as Jaymee, and as a father he could understand David's motives only too well.

'I have never, thank heavens, been faced with that dreadful situation in my own family, but I would certainly be advocating on behalf of my children and I would expect all parents to do that. It's part of being a good parent. At no point has anybody in this authority ever criticized him or any member of the family for taking the position they have. It's a perfectly understandable position to adopt.'

But whatever Stephen Thornton might have done as a parent had he found himself in the same position as David, the arguments put forward in court on the Health Authority's behalf had to be those of an NHS manager, and as far as Cambridge Health Authority was concerned, Jaymee Bowen wasn't the only individual whose needs they had to consider when deciding how to spend their money.

'If we spend money on one patient, it's money that isn't available for other patients,' he said. 'And in this particular case, when we looked at what the value for money would be, we saw an example of treatment that was neither effective nor

appropriate, so in that sense treatment that would be technically a waste of money compared with what it could be spent
on in other parts of the health service. That's not to say that
it wouldn't be right for her to receive treatment. The question
is: should we as a health authority, operating on behalf of the
taxpayer, make the decision to treat?'

Ever since Stephen Thornton and Ron Zimmern made the
decision not to fund Jaymee's treatment, they have argued
consistently that it was a legitimate decision taken in a legitimate way. 'Many public authorities hide behind a veil of
secrecy, but I honestly believe we came out whiter than white,'
Mr Thornton said.

At the end of the first day in court, neither David nor his
lawyers had any idea about which way the judgement might
go. They would have to wait until the next morning when Mr
Justice Laws would give his ruling. As they left the High
Court that evening, a few flashbulbs went off and the evening
news had pictures of David and Ossie walking away from the
court. But it was nothing compared with what they'd have to
face the next day.

That evening, Ossie, David and Rita discussed tactics. But
for the moment, until judgement was delivered, everything
was on hold.

The next morning, Ossie and David left the house at eight
o'clock. They had to be back at the High Court by ten o'clock
and they needed to go to their barrister's chambers first. Rita
would take Jaymee to the Royal Marsden for her blood transfusion. Somehow, the stakes seemed higher today. The judge
had heard the arguments and made his decision. They would
just have to be patient until he was ready to deliver it. Rose
was waiting for them outside the courtroom, her arms full of
legal documents. But the judge wasn't ready. It was almost an
hour later that they started filing into court.

'We were all going in and suddenly David grabbed me and said, "You're going to sit next to me, aren't you?"' Rose recalled. 'I hadn't particularly thought about it but I said yes and he said, "I want to sit next to you because when I collapse I want it to be you I collapse on."'

By now, the media were beginning to get interested in Jaymee's case and there were about twenty reporters crowded at the back of the courtroom to hear Mr Justice Laws's decision. It took him fifty minutes to read.

'Of all human rights, most people would accord the most precious place to the right to life itself,' he began. After reviewing all the evidence that had been presented to him in court, the judge began to make his own views clear. David held his breath.

The judge continued. 'If the necessary funds are made available for Dr Gravett to embark on B's treatment, she would enjoy what I will call a worthwhile chance of life. It may be very modest. It may be less than 10 per cent. But to anyone confronting the prospect of extinction in a few weeks, such a chance of longer, perhaps much longer, survival must be unimaginably precious.'

'Every word made perfect sense,' David said. Eloquent and concise, the judge's words expressed just what was at stake in a case which by mid-morning that Friday was beginning to touch a national nerve. The right to life, as part of the European Convention on Human Rights, should, the judge argued, be regarded as a fundamental principle of English common law, not merely as a 'moral or political aspiration'.

If Jaymee had been an adult, her views would have had to be respected by the Health Authority. Just because she was a child, the judge said, why should the right to decide be handed to her doctors? It should be her father who decided on her behalf because 'he has duties and responsibilities to her shared by no one else'.

David sat beside Rose, listening intently to every word. Just before 11.45 a.m., the judge announced his decision. 'Where the question is whether the life of a ten-year-old child might be saved, by however slim a chance, the responsible authority must in my judgement do more than toll the bell of tight resources. They must explain the priorities that have led them to decline to fund the treatment. They have not adequately done so here.'

The decision taken by Cambridge Health Authority must be quashed, the judge pronounced. That did not mean that the authority could be ordered to pay for the treatment, simply that they must reconsider their decision, taking into account what he had said in his judgement. It was precisely the ruling David's legal team had hoped for.

But there was barely time for a moment's celebration. Immediately the judge finished speaking, the barrister for Cambridge Health Authority was on his feet saying they wanted to appeal. Their case would be heard that afternoon and the judges who would hear it wanted to read all the relevant papers by two o'clock. As there were three of them, and more than a hundred pages of documents, that meant that apart from discussing how their case should be argued in the Court of Appeal, there were three hundred photocopies to be done. There was less than two hours to go before they were all due back in court.

Then they found there was another force to contend with: the press were becoming ever more interested in Jaymee's case and they wanted to talk to David.

'We came out of court at a quarter to twelve to be faced with a complete rim of reporters asking questions,' Rose said. 'At that stage we were saying we can't comment because we don't know what the Court of Appeal is going to say and we've got a lot of work to do between now and then.'

To protect Jaymee from the truth about her illness, David

had asked the judge to impose an order protecting her identity and that of her family before the court case began. 'I didn't want Jaymee damaged in any way by what was going on so I needed to protect her the best I could and that was the only way to do it. Had Jaymee read or found out that this was her we were talking about, she would then have known that she was going to die. She would have known that her fate rested on what happened in court.'

From then until the order was lifted almost nine months later, Jaymee was known only as Child B – the little girl for whom rationing health care had become a reality. Every time David or his father appeared on television, their faces were covered by little black blobs. It was a perfect story. But the extent of media interest took the Bowens completely by surprise. Their thoughts had been entirely focused on Jaymee. Now Child B was fast becoming a celebrity. The story was the main item on every news bulletin that day.

At the Royal Marsden Hospital, where she was with Jaymee, Rita began to realize how difficult it was going to be to impose a media blackout on Jaymee herself, the very person the anonymity order was designed to protect.

'There was a television near Jaymee's bed and I could see it was the main item,' Rita said. 'I looked up and there were David and Ossie on the screen walking out of the court. I tried to turn the television away from Jaymee, and then suddenly someone else was put in the bed next to her and turned on the little radio.' The story was on there too.

Jaymee listened carefully as she heard the news item discussing the case of Child B. Then she turned to her grandmother. 'She said, "Oh what a shame, I think they really should treat that little girl. I bet you if she was British she would have been treated. Poor thing." Those were her words,' Rita said. 'And I thought, Oh no. I couldn't believe she had heard but she had heard and she had picked it up straight away. I think she thought it was a little foreign girl who'd come into the country. I thought, My goodness, if only she knew it was her they were talking about.'

Jaymee had assumed that Child B couldn't be British because, if she was, the NHS would be treating her. To Rita, it seemed to demonstrate an extraordinary degree of perception for a ten-year-old child. When David rang her that lunchtime, Rita told him what Jaymee had said. Suddenly he understood why his daughter's case was attracting so much attention.

Jaymee says she remembers nothing about that day. She was weak and being kept alive by a combination of blood transfusions and drugs. But six months later, when David had told Jaymee the truth about Child B, I was able to ask her for the first time what she would have done if she had known how ill she was at the time and how small her chance of a cure appeared to be. She looked me straight in the eye and said with the courage and conviction that were to astonish those who later saw Jaymee on television, 'I would have gone to court and stood there right in front of them and said, "No matter what it takes, I am going to go through this and I'm going to get better." '

When David, Ossie and Rose came out of the barrister's chambers after lunch to make their way to the Appeal Court, a barrage of reporters was waiting for them on the other side of the road.

'It's quite frightening to be in the middle of that, even when they're on your side,' Rose said. 'Bruce the barrister was saying sorry we can't comment. I don't know whether David even took it in. He was like an automaton at that stage and I had to drag him across the zebra crossing towards the court.'

That afternoon, the Health Authority's lawyers talked money. 'From a legal point of view, it was obviously the way the case had to be argued,' Rose said. 'Courts have always said we can't allocate public resources however much we would like to, and it was obvious from Mr Justice Laws's decision that that was the way to challenge it. The Health Authority's barrister had moved up and down a spectrum of how difficult money was. In the Court of Appeal he laid it on with a trowel.'

Back in Cambridge, Stephen Thornton and his colleagues had been anxiously waiting to hear from their lawyers. Instead they found themselves relying on the press to let them know what had happened in court that morning. When they learned that Mr Justice Laws had ordered them to reconsider their decision, Stephen Thornton called an emergency meeting of as many members of the Health Authority as he could gather for three o'clock that afternoon. If the High Court had told them to reconsider, that was precisely what they would do.

When they eventually managed to speak to their solicitors and were advised to appeal, they assumed the case would be heard the following week and that in the meantime they would be able to muster their arguments.

'So we went ahead with our meeting,' Stephen Thornton said. 'We reviewed our decision-making step by step with Ron Zimmern explaining why he had done what he had done on the Health Authority's behalf.' It wasn't until after the meeting had started that they learned that at precisely the same time as they were reviewing their decision, their lawyers were on their feet in the Appeal Court arguing that Mr Justice Laws's ruling should be overturned.

'By then we realized that we were going to have to make a statement,' Mr Thornton said. 'We decided that if the Appeal Court upheld our case, it was important that we tell as much of our side of the story as possible. We knew there was an issue here as well as a story, and by tea-time on Friday we'd all agreed that we discuss the issues as much as possible in whatever public statements we made.'

The three Appeal Court judges included the Master of the Rolls, Sir Thomas Bingham, one of the most senior lawyers in the land. From twenty past two until ten to five, they listened to the arguments put forward by both sides. Then they rose and retired to reach their decision, leaving David, Ossie, Rose and the rest of the legal team sitting in the courtroom surrounded by reporters. 'It felt like forever,' Rose said.

For much of the day, reporters had been passing pieces of paper to David in the courtroom begging him to talk to them. 'They'd say, "I'm from such and such a paper, we would like to speak to you about this. Here is my home number, my pager number," and so on. I think I could probably reach the editor of every single national newspaper wherever they are. No one wanted to be outbid by anyone else. They wanted to get the story first.'

Twenty-five minutes later, the judges returned to the court and Sir Thomas Bingham began reading the judgement. It took three quarters of an hour and at first it was impossible to tell which way it would go. 'No decision affecting human life is one that can be regarded with other than the greatest seriousness,' he said, but immediately made it clear that the courts could rule only on whether decisions were lawful, not whether they were right or wrong.

Again David thought about the person whose life depended on what the judge would say next. Again he looked at Jaymee's photograph. Then suddenly, as Sir Thomas continued reading, David began to realize that things were no longer going their way. It was common knowledge, the judge said, that the health service was under constant pressure to make ends meet. Health authorities could never provide all the treatments or buy all the expensive medical equipment they would like. 'Difficult and agonizing judgements have to be made as to how a limited budget is best allocated to the maximum advantage of the maximum number of patients.

David Bowen with his daughters, Charlotte, aged eighteen months (*left*), and Jaymee, nearly three (*right*), in Trafalgar Square, 1987.

August 1990: Jaymee's sixth birthday, one month before her
cancer was first diagnosed.

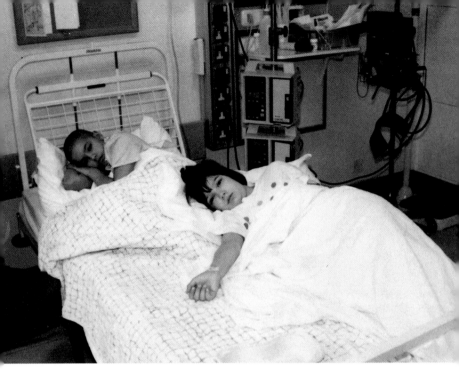

March 1994: Jaymee and Charlotte in the Royal Marsden Hospital after Jaymee's bone marrow transplant.

Charlotte celebrates her eighth birthday in Addenbrooke's Hospital with Luke (*right, standing behind her*), stepmother Debbie Bowen, David and Ossie (*standing left to right*), and Jaymee, seated centre with Rita.

(*Left*) Jaymee in 1993: the school photograph her father took to court.

(*Below*) March 1995: Jaymee with Dr Peter Gravett at the Portland Hospital at the start of her treatment.

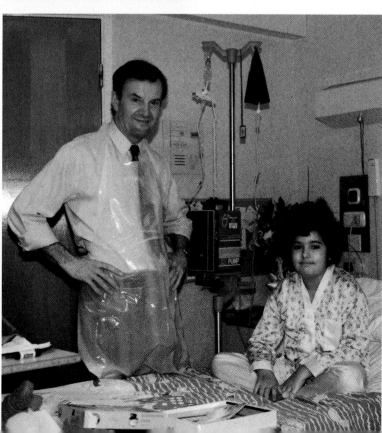

Date 29/3/95

My hair has started to fall
out and I am not very happy
about it. I am now affraid to
Wash my hair and dry it after-
Wards because I just know I will
end up with a towel full of hair
and a head with none on it.
I hope to get out of hospital
for a day or two some time
this week but my blood count
may be too low in which case
I will have to wait another week

Jaymee
xxx

Speak again
Tomorrow.

An extract from Jaymee's diary.

David and Jaymee in June 1995, half-way through her experimental treatment (photo: Mike Robinson).

A precious moment: Jaymee on a half-term outing to the fair (photo: Mike Robinson).

Waiting for the treatment to work: Jaymee in hospital after another dose of Charlotte's cells (photo: Mike Robinson).

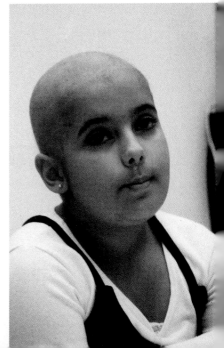

9 September 1995: the author with Jaymee after recording her interview for *Panorama* (photo: Mike Robinson).

Jaymee's grandparents, Rita and Ossie, at home, November 1995.

One year on: Jaymee in February 1996 (photo: Mike Robinson).

That is not a judgement which the court can make.'

Rose saw what was happening too. 'It was about the last five minutes that I realized it had gone against us. I looked at David and I didn't really know what to do. I didn't know whether to hold his hand. He kept looking at me and I kept looking at him and then his hands started shaking and I grabbed hold of them and in the last few minutes I just held on to him.'

The judge's final sentence echoed in their ears. 'While I have every possible sympathy with "B", I feel bound to regard this as an attempt, wholly understandable but none the less misguided, to involve the court in a field of activity where it is not fitted to make any decision favourable to the patient.'

That was it. 'It sunk in word by word by word exactly as he said it. I thought that even though he wasn't doing it willingly, this man was signing off my daughter's life,' David said.

The three judges got up and left the court, leaving David, Ossie and their lawyers in stunned silence surrounded by reporters. The immediate problem was how to deal with them. In a moment they would be after David, and Rose realized he wasn't capable of saying anything.

'We decided that I should take David back to the barrister's chambers while Michael Sinclair, the other solicitor involved in the case, would stop and talk to the press and try and hold them off,' said Rose. 'I grabbed hold of David and I had to get my arm right round him to move him because he wasn't doing anything. If you pushed him one way, he'd walk that way; if you pushed him the other way, he'd walk that way.'

For the first few minutes everything went to plan. David and Rose left the courtroom and headed towards the great hall of the High Court and towards the front entrance. Theirs was the last case to finish that Friday afternoon, so the building was practically empty and most of the lights were out.

'We were walking fast and for the first few minutes it was

just the two of us, but suddenly we heard all these footsteps on the flagstones and it sounded like a stampede,' said Rose. The reporters had realized where they were and were desperate to reach them before they left the building. But in front of the High Court, television cameras and photographers were out in force too. David and Rose left the building to be greeted by a barrage of flashbulbs and lights. There were reporters everywhere, three-deep across the entrance.

'It was a total shock,' David said. 'When I came out, all I could see were cameras and photographers. The first row was kneeling down, the second row was a little bit higher. The next one was standing up and the ones at the back were holding the cameras. All I could see was flash, flash, flash, flash, and they wouldn't move.'

At that point it made little difference to him whether the press were on his side or not, even though they were to play an important role in securing the funding for Jaymee's treatment simply by bringing her case to the public's attention. 'All I knew was that we had lost,' David said.

Somehow they pushed their way through the crowd of photographers, with Rose still pulling David along by the arm. They started walking in the direction of the barrister's chambers, leaving Michael Sinclair to make a statement to the press. 'We got back into chambers and all hell was breaking loose in there,' Rose said. 'It was probably five minutes, perhaps ten, since the judge had finished speaking and there were already faxes coming in from the *Sun*, the *News of the World* and the *Daily Mirror*, offering money, and there were others who just wanted a comment. All David wanted to do was to phone the hospital and see how Jaymee was.' But there was one fax which interested them more than all the others. It was from a highly reputable firm of London solicitors and it made an offer which seemed to be the answer to all their prayers. The solicitors said they had £75,000 available immediately for Jaymee's treatment. The source of the funds wished to remain anonymous, but the money was there if they wanted it. Throughout the day, these solicitors had been trying to get messages to Michael Sinclair in court, asking him to contact them. But it was only now that he had time to fax them back asking them to set out what they were offering and on what terms.

'We sat for some considerable time waiting for a reply,' Rose said. 'Then a sheet of paper was faxed through with a handwritten list of what they had in mind, for example that Jaymee's medical bills should be sent directly to them for payment. Michael was satisfied that it was a proper offer.'

There were other offers too, notably from the controversial chairman of Harrods, Mohammed Al-Fayed, but David and his lawyers felt the best offer at that moment was from the anonymous donor, so they agreed to accept it. Time was running out for Jaymee and it meant she could be admitted to hospital almost immediately to start her treatment.

'It seemed that although we'd lost in court, we'd won after all,' said Rose. When they left the barrister's chambers at about 8.20 p.m., there were more reporters in the hall below and halfway up the stairs. Still reluctant to say anything that night, David, Ossie and Rose set off on foot towards Temple tube station because David was anxious to get back to his parents' house, where Jaymee was waiting for him after her blood transfusion. By the steps of the Underground, the reporters finally disappeared and Rose said goodnight to David and Ossie.

'And that was the end of the day,' Rose said. 'I didn't think we'd failed because there was some argument we didn't pursue, but I felt the system had failed and I felt collectively part of that.'

'I knew we were going to have problems,' David said. 'I knew what Justice Laws had done. The effect on the National

Health Service would have been catastrophic if the ruling had been upheld in the Appeal Court, so it had to be turned down.'

Even if the law had failed them, the collective power of the press and the generosity of the anonymous donor meant that Jaymee would get the chance her father so desperately wanted for her and believed she deserved. That was all that mattered now.

8

A Private Doctor and an Ethical Divide

When David and Ossie got home that evening, Rita was wait-ing anxiously to hear what had happened in court. They sat up talking until three o'clock in the morning and, as usual, none of the adults slept very much that night. They knew only too well that the money had come just in time for Jaymee. If the court case had been a week later, she would probably have lost the chance of being treated by Dr Gravett too. He had to leave for a medical conference in Switzerland on 18 March and would be away for a week. Jaymee was now so ill it is unlikely she would have survived until his return.

Peter Gravett had told David that Monday was the last day he could admit her to hospital before he went away. Jaymee's chemotherapy would last four days and he wanted to make sure it was finished before he left the country.

It was, said Rita with typical understatement, an 'anxious weekend'. The cancer cells were multiplying so fast it was obvious that however many blood transfusions she had, they were now only eking out small amounts of extra time. The family began to wonder if she would even last the weekend.

'We were all looking forward to Monday because she was just getting worse. You could see it,' Rita said.

There was another issue for the family to contend with too. On the Saturday morning, Child B was still front-page news. In spite of the offer from the anonymous donor, a number of tabloid newspapers were also queuing up to pay the bill and get exclusive rights to Jaymee's story in return. The entire front page of the *Daily Mirror* was devoted to a large picture of the backs of David and Rose as she helped him out of the High Court. '*Daily Mirror* Offers To Pay For Dying Girl's Op' blazed the headline. 'What Price A Life?' asked another tabloid.

Somehow Jaymee's family had to make sure she knew nothing about it. 'Most of the time we spent keeping the news away from her,' Rita said. 'We bought the newspapers and then hid them and we manned the phone to make sure she didn't answer it.' Jaymee and Charlotte couldn't understand why Ossie and Rita were refusing to watch the television news. It was their usual nightly ritual and the children would have to sit and watch it with them. But not that weekend. This was not the moment for Jaymee to discover the truth.

On the Monday morning, the whole family was up early. Jaymee was tired and lethargic and unable to walk more than fifty yards without stopping for breath. Nevertheless, they went shopping on their way to the hospital and bought Jaymee and Charlotte some new clothes so that they would look presentable for the photographs they were to have taken that day.

During the weekend, David had come to an arrangement with the *Daily Mirror*, giving them exclusive access to the story. In return, they agreed to set up a fund to raise more money for Jaymee's treatment and for other children with leukaemia. The newspaper had offered to send a car to collect them from Ossie and Rita's house, but David agreed to meet them in town instead.

'We did the deal with the *Mirror* because the scale of the publicity was so vast that we couldn't see how we would get in or out of hospital or anywhere without being mobbed and that would have tipped the whole thing off to Jaymee,' David said.

Fortunately the press did not know that David, Jaymee and Charlotte had been staying with Rita and Ossie. Instead they went to David's house near Cambridge, to his solicitor's house, to the local post office and to Jaymee's school trying to find them. Once David had agreed to talk to the *Daily Mirror*, that newspaper had a vested interest in protecting its story from all the other media, especially on that Monday morning, when Jaymee was to start her treatment at the Portland Hospital.

'They told everyone that we were going to the London Clinic so that we could get into the Portland unnoticed. We went in the back entrance of the hospital just to make sure because there were still some people out the front. It was quite funny,' David said.

Jaymee was being treated at the Portland Hospital because the London Clinic, where Peter Gravett does most of his work, is not licensed to treat children and so has no special facilities for looking after them. As Jaymee could be in hospital for up to a month, it was important that she should be cared for in an environment where there were specialist children's nurses and surroundings more suited to her needs.

Jaymee was shown to her room on the fifth floor, which is entirely devoted to children. In appearance, it is like many NHS children's units, with colourful friezes and pictures on the walls and a large playroom full of toys and books. On the door of every bedroom is a specially painted nameplate so that every child feels welcome. The additional luxuries which marked this out as a private hospital were the wall-to-wall carpeting, twenty-four-hour room service and a television and telephone in every room.

Once the family were safely inside, the rest of the media descended. 'There were huge television aerials being extended outside the hospital and we kept the curtains pulled. It was crazy and it just went on and on,' David said.

Shortly after Jaymee had arrived, Peter Gravett came round to the Portland to visit her. He had been completely taken by surprise by the enormous media interest in his new patient. He says he was under the impression that even though the NHS had refused to pay for Jaymee's treatment, the Bowens had private medical insurance which would cover the cost of her care. As far as he was concerned, the bills would be paid. What he didn't know was that the insurance company had also said no, thinking presumably that Jaymee did not represent a 'good risk'.

'The first I knew was when reporters started turning up outside the London Clinic and outside my consulting rooms in Harley Street on the Monday morning wanting to talk to me,' Dr Gravett said. For the next few days he was besieged by the press every time he left the building. If they couldn't talk to Child B, talking to her doctor was the next best thing.

Carolyn Meunier, the managing director of Accountability, the public relations firm which represents the London Clinic, had realized three days earlier that Child B was going to be a very big story. On the day of the court case she arrived at the London Clinic for a meeting to discover a fleet of radio and television vans on either side of the street and seven or eight journalists waiting in reception.

She spent the weekend deciding how best to deal with the deluge of inquiries that started coming in, not just from Britain but from around the world. Jaymee's story had touched a national and international nerve. She had come to symbolize what was being portrayed, rightly or wrongly, as a cultural change in the National Health Service. If a ten-year-old child could be denied life-saving treatment on the grounds of cost, who would be next on the rationing list?

'I have been in public relations for twenty years and I can honestly say that I have never handled such a phenomenal story that has just gone on and on,' said Carolyn Meunier.

The journalists wanted to know everything, from the most complicated medical details to how many dolls and toys Jaymee had brought with her to hospital and what she had chosen to eat from the extensive menu at the Portland. The fact that she was known only as Child B made the story even more interesting.

'Our telephone lines and faxes were almost constantly engaged by continuous media inquiries night and day with requests for interviews and for us to reveal who Child B actually was. Journalistic approaches ranged from the sophisticated to the cunning, the blunt, the aggressive and the downright rude,' Carolyn Meunier told me. 'Some of the major media, faced with relentless deadlines, even attempted to threaten my career – two journalists said that they would write condemnatory letters to the Managing Director of Accountability because I refused to compromise Child B's identity. When they learnt that I *was* the Managing Director, they didn't know what to do.'

For Peter Gravett, a doctor more accustomed to caring for his patients than giving press conferences, it was all completely unexpected. 'Initially it was actually quite difficult to cope in terms of finding enough hours in the day to handle all the inquiries and answer the questions and carry on treating other patients,' he said. 'But there was a certain novelty to being exposed to so much publicity, which gave me enough impetus to see me through it, at least for a few days.'

David had placed all his confidence in the slightly built and quietly spoken doctor in his late forties who had been so highly recommended by Professor Goldman, and he was anxious that Jaymee should share that trust. She had been treated by so many doctors in the last five years that each time she met a new one her instinct was to be suspicious.

But after her initial impression that he was 'odd', Jaymee began to like the man she called Peter and saw him as an ally rather than as someone who would subject her to treatments without asking her first. 'As soon as I started to get confident with him I thought, "Well, if I'm going to get better, I might as well get better with him because he seems to know what he's doing."'

What she liked about Peter Gravett was the way in which he involved her in discussions about her treatment right from the start. 'I like to be asked things. If they're going to give something to me, I like at least to have an opinion about it,' she said. 'When I started being treated by Peter I got the first choice about what I wanted to do. He said I could either have chemotherapy to get rid of this thing or I could have another treatment which would take longer and probably wouldn't kill it off and I'd have to have the chemotherapy anyway. So I just went for the chemotherapy. It was good because I hadn't had a choice before.'

The choice Peter Gravett had given Jaymee was between having a high dose of powerful chemotherapy which he hoped would get her leukaemia into remission, and being given drugs to try to persuade the leukaemia or 'blast' cells to transform themselves into normal blood cells. The first option would mean staying in hospital, the second could be done entirely on an out-patient basis. Despite her dislike of hospitals, Jaymee decided it was better to get the treatment over with as quickly as possible.

'There were times when I absolutely refused to have things because they wouldn't tell me what it was and how it was going to affect me. It's only this time that I've been with Peter that Daddy's explained practically everything that he's going to do,' she told me.

David, a man not easily impressed, was also won over by what he regarded as Peter Gravett's quiet confidence. Here was someone who was willing to give his daughter another chance and to pull out every stop that modern medicine could offer to try to find a cure. And he was prepared to treat David as an equal. They discussed exactly what Peter was planning to do every step of the way, so that it seemed to David they were embarking on a journey of medical discovery together. Whatever happened, David felt that at least Peter would be able to extend the life which had been on the point of being snuffed out.

Dr Gravett planned to start giving Jaymee chemotherapy the following day, but first he needed to give her a new Hickman line through which the drugs could be administered. It was the third time she'd had a line put in. It would mean having another scar on her chest when it was eventually removed and another anaesthetic to have it put in. Jaymee was terrified of anaesthetics. 'Every time I've had an operation, I've wondered the same thing. Am I going to wake up? Will I ever see light again, because there are people who have had anaesthetics who haven't woken up from them?'

Rita and Ossie stayed at the hospital all day helping Jaymee to settle in. They finally left at one o'clock in the morning. David and Charlotte stayed the night. It was a familiar routine.

At a quarter past four the following afternoon, Peter Gravett issued a statement to the press: 'I have come to the London Clinic via the Portland Hospital to check on the first day's progress and found the patient sitting up in bed on the telephone to one of her friends, while simultaneously watching a video and ordering her lunches and dinners from a stack of menus for the next four or five days. She started chemotherapy at twelve o'clock and will finish at seven o'clock this evening, and so far there have been no adverse effects at all – it certainly hasn't taken the edge off her appetite . . . we don't anticipate any problems during the remainder of her treatment, which will finish at the weekend.'

It was a deliberately positive image but typical of the way

in which Jaymee approached being in hospital. She rarely complained and hardly ever indulged in self-pity, preferring to keep her feelings to herself. It was easier that way. But underneath that positive façade, Jaymee was confused.

She still had no idea how ill she was, and finding herself back in hospital facing losing her hair for the fourth time filled her with horror. She knew she was going to have more chemotherapy but not why. Because David had taken the decision that she must not be told how close to death she was, he'd simply told her she'd got a 'bug in her blood'. 'I was thinking, "Oh no, here we go." I thought it would just be something very slight that they could get rid of with some antibiotics and I went into hospital and found that I had to have more chemotherapy.

'That didn't exactly make me feel any better because I'd just spent the last few months growing my hair and it didn't make me feel any better that I had to go and lose it again.'

She also faced the prospect of being in isolation if she developed an infection after the chemotherapy. Because the drugs attack healthy blood cells as well as cancer cells, resistance to infection falls dramatically.

In fact this was precisely what happened. Jaymee's chemotherapy was over by the end of her first week in hospital. Then she developed an infection and was in isolation for ten days. 'In hospital, when you're in isolation, there are no exceptions,' Jaymee said. 'You get your food brought to you. You get it taken away. You're just stuck in there. That's it. Not allowed out. Nothing.'

'After the first twenty-four hours in hospital, it becomes a blur,' David said. 'Someone could tell you it's a Saturday and it'll be a Friday and you wouldn't know and you wouldn't care. You are just there with your child, going through an experience with her and you're powerless to help. You tend not to sleep and be very agitated and very on edge and you get more run down as time goes on.'

To help pass the time, David brought in a video camera to make a record of Jaymee's time in the Portland. In the first pictures Jaymee still has her hair – an unruly mop of dark curls framing her face. At times she seems cheerful, smiling at the camera or playing games with David. At others she is obviously miserable. One shot shows her curled up in bed with the sheet pulled around her. A tear rolls slowly down her cheek.

On 29 March, she wrote in her diary: 'My hair has started to fall out and I am not very happy about it. I am now afraid to wash my hair and dry it afterwards because I just know I will end up with a towel full of hair and a head with none on it. I hope to get out of hospital for a day or two sometime this week but my blood count may be too low, in which case I will have to wait another week.' Jaymee couldn't bear the thought of her hair falling out bit by bit, so she and David made a decision. He would shave it all off at once.

The video camera recorded it all. 'Just do it,' Jaymee tells her father impatiently. David tugs at the hair and Jaymee shouts angrily, 'Don't pull the stuff out, cut it.' Bit by bit, all the hair comes out until Jaymee is transformed into the stereotyped image of a cancer sufferer, her dark eyes now appearing disproportionately large in her face. This was my first image of her when I met her for the first time, almost a month later.

'Hair brings out your face,' Jaymee told me. 'I know some-one at school who is always brushing her hair. She brushes it at least six times a day. She would say, "Show me a mirror," then she would stand there and she'd brush it and she wouldn't stop until it looked good. And she'd just stand there and brush it for ages and ages and ages and then she'd say, "Jaymee, does my hair look all right?" I'd say, "Your hair always looks all right." In a way it's made me envious of people who have hair. They're lucky they've got any. It will take me two years to grow something the size of a little bush.'

Every day she was in hospital, Ossie and Rita took it in turns to visit Jaymee. Ossie would come in the morning, bringing Charlotte with him, and Rita would come after work. In spite of the room service on tap at the Portland, Rita would often cook for Jaymee at home and bring the food in with her, just as she had done when Jaymee had had her bone marrow transplant. Jaymee's favourite dishes were curry, spaghetti bolognese and macaroni cheese. Whatever she felt like eating that day, her grandmother would do her best to provide it.

Although David was convinced he'd done the right thing by fighting for Jaymee's treatment, he, like the rest of the family, was also anxious about what lay ahead. 'Time had been slipping away from us and once we'd got the money and Jaymee had started her treatment, I think all the questions started,' Rita said. 'Who could say if we were doing the right thing? And I kept looking at her all the time, thinking about what she was going through, and I think David was worried about that all the time.'

However optimistic David tried to be, for Jaymee's sake as well as his own, no one was pretending that the chance of success was high. All that Peter Gravett had agreed to do that Jaymee's NHS doctors had refused was to try and get her leukaemia into remission again using chemotherapy. He'd told David the chances of this were between 10 and 20 per cent. He'd also told him quite clearly that unless Jaymee was in remission, he couldn't justify giving her another bone marrow transplant any more than her original doctors could. The risks were too high. The difference between Peter Gravett and Jaymee's NHS doctors was they believed that because her leukaemia was now so resistant to drugs the chance of her going into remission again was 'remote'.

They thought that by ignoring the consensus of opinion among child cancer specialists in the UK, David Bowen had crossed an ethical Rubicon. On one side there were the NHS children's cancer doctors, on the other there were doctors specializing in adult leukaemia and those like Peter Gravett working in the private sector who were willing to give more aggressive treatment than the children's doctors thought acceptable. In their view, the way Jaymee's case was being handled justified their belief that she should have been allowed to die with dignity.

There are twenty-two specialist children's cancer centres in the UK and they all try to adhere to the same basic code of what they consider to be ethically acceptable as far as treating children is concerned. Proposed new treatments for children, including the drugs involved, are subjected to rigorous scrutiny by ethics committees in every hospital, a procedure which does not exist in the private sector.

None of the NHS specialist children's units were prepared to say they genuinely believed it was in Jaymee's best interests to be submitted to the ordeal of more chemotherapy, and perhaps another bone marrow transplant, when the chance of a cure was so small and the course of treatment proposed still officially classified as experimental.

From the start, the UK Children's Cancer Study Group, the official body of children's cancer specialists, was extremely critical of Dr Gravett for agreeing to treat Jaymee. 'I and, I know, many of my colleagues are unhappy at the idea of any child with cancer being treated outside a specialist centre,' Professor Pinkerton said, 'in particular, a child for whom conventional treatment has failed and who is being considered for experimental research treatment.'

Professor Pinkerton was also concerned about the level of

care Jaymee might receive in a private hospital compared with the NHS. 'The risk would be that if she became very unwell, the level of nursing expertise, the level of junior doctor expertise, the general level of paediatric input, particularly by people experienced in supporting children through this sort of toxicity, all that could be missing.'

I asked him if he thought Peter Gravett was wrong to take Jaymee on. 'I wouldn't have done it, no,' he replied.

In fact, the Portland Hospital's children's unit has facilities very similar to those offered at Great Ormond Street Hospital, one of the best-known NHS children's hospitals in the world. There are junior doctors on duty at all times at the Portland, some of whom also work at Great Ormond Street. All the nurses at the Portland are specialist children's nurses and some of the senior staff have been trained in cancer care.

With a case as controversial as Jaymee's, it was inevitable that a certain amount of medical politics would be involved in the debate about her treatment. As far as the UK Children's Cancer Study Group was concerned, it was important to maintain its position as the principal body which devised the treatment programmes and ethical parameters for children with cancer. And that meant, by and large, testing new treatments on adults before trying them on children.

But for Peter Gravett and a number of other specialists in adult leukaemia, there was an element of inflexibility about the position taken by the UKCCSG. Their view was that if a child was to be allowed to die simply because a new treatment hadn't completed all the clinical trials in adults, that indicated a conservatism which would lead to avoidable deaths or, at least, shortened lives.

These were the agonizing medical and ethical dilemmas in which David Bowen found himself caught up. As far as he was concerned, the NHS had abandoned Jaymee even though he had done everything within his powers to persuade it to treat her. If his last remaining port of call was the private sector, so be it. To him this was not a question of ethics committees and medical protocols but a matter of life or death. As long as he believed Jaymee could tolerate the treatment, he was prepared to put her through it.

'I think if there was ever a child who scored well on what she's gone through and what she's done, and the response to drugs, and her zest and appetite for life, this is the child. And I will at least honour her by giving her the chance that I feel she really needs,' he told me.

During the long days and nights David spent with Jaymee in the Portland Hospital, he had time to reflect on everything that had happened in the past two months, and, in his bleakest moments, he admitted to himself what he had not been able to admit to his parents. 'What if the treatment were to fail? How would you cross that bridge with Jaymee? You still have to make the normal sorts of everyday decisions as well as thinking about how much a funeral is going to cost. Would I bury her or cremate her? Those sorts of things.'

But Jaymee and her sister knew nothing of what was going on in their father's mind. As usual, David kept his emotions to himself. When he'd been crying, he wore dark glasses.

Yet within days of starting chemotherapy, Jaymee was looking better and seemed to have more energy. Once her infection was under control and she was out of isolation, she got up and wandered down the corridor to the playroom where she could draw and paint. She started designing a large mural for Easter and painting Easter eggs with Charlotte. On sunny days she was allowed to go to Regent's Park just across the road from the hospital. But it was still too early to find out if the chemotherapy had worked. They would have to wait another two weeks before Dr Gravett could test Jaymee's bone marrow to see if her leukaemia had gone into remission. There was nothing the Bowens could do but wait and hope.

Although everyone was telling her that she was getting better, Jaymee says she felt the same as when she'd arrived at the Portland. 'I remember one of the doctors coming in and saying, "Jaymee, you're making progress," and I thought, Oh yeah! I didn't really feel as if I was at all. I was still getting the shakes and shivers and really high temperatures. It was very depressing.'

'Get Well' cards started arriving in large numbers from family and friends and Jaymee's classmates at school. There were lots of others too, from members of the public, addressed to 'Little B', the name she'd been given by the *Daily Mirror*. However hard the family tried to hide them from Jaymee, it was inevitable that one day some of these cards would slip through the net and arrive in her bedroom. Not surprisingly, she was puzzled. 'Who is little B?' she asked Rita after two cards had been delivered to her one day. Thinking quickly, Rita replied, 'Little B is little Bowen. We're the Big Bowens and you are the little one.'

But Jaymee wasn't entirely satisfied with her grandmother's reply. 'When you get a card that has got a name in it that's not a name you're familiar with, like Child B and your name is Jaymee, you think something's happened here. And you just know that there's something that's happened you should know about. With this family that means something has happened that is obviously quite important.'

It was to be another six months before she was told the truth. However, it had taken Jaymee's classmates no time at all to work out that she was the Child B in the newspapers, and they were devastated. 'The whole class came in in floods of tears after they'd heard the story on the radio and seen the newspapers,' said Felicia Goss, Jaymee's form teacher. 'They said, "Is it Jaymee, miss?" The children had thought she was cured.'

It was difficult for the school to know what to do because of the need to keep the truth from Jaymee. 'There were queues of children at my door wanting to go and visit her and to take cards and drawings, and that was very difficult because Jaymee didn't know she was Child B,' David Pugh, the headteacher, told me.

So the school had to instruct the children to make anonymous cards which had to be vetted by Felicia to make sure that no one gave the game away. The staff were distraught at the way in which the story had broken, but long before David had been to court they had been advised by professional counsellors from Addenbrooke's Hospital about how to help the children come to terms with the death of one of their classmates.

Even though this was the same hospital which had refused Jaymee more treatment, David Pugh says the counsellors were very helpful. 'They were at pains to make sure that the staff who came for counselling firmly believed that Jaymee's last weeks would be as pain-free and happy as possible,' he said.

'They explained the likely outcome and the reasons for not treating her,' Felicia Goss told me. 'They said she might suddenly start bleeding and not feeling well and that would be the beginning of the end. We didn't think she'd survive.'

The staff discussed what the school might do to provide a suitable memorial for Jaymee, perhaps plant a tree in the grounds or set up a Jaymee Bowen award. It wasn't the first time they had had to face losing one of their pupils. A boy called Michael had died of leukaemia several years before, and the thought that it was going to happen again was all the more distressing for them.

Whatever she may have suspected in private, officially Jaymee knew nothing, and that was how David wanted it to be. He wanted her to put every ounce of energy into getting better.

When Peter Gravett agreed to take Jaymee on, it was in the hope that giving her more chemotherapy would get her cancer into remission and buy everyone extra time in which to decide what to do next. A second bone marrow transplant was his least preferred option, even though he had promised to consider it. But the question which weighed heavily on his mind was whether there were any other options that would involve less trauma and risk than a second transplant but which would have some chance of prolonging Jaymee's life.

A conversation on a train provided him with the answer.

9

A Guinea Pig?

STATEMENT BY DR PETER GRAVETT:

UPDATE ON CHILD B 14.00 HOURS 18 MARCH 1995

Child B settled into the Portland Hospital well and commenced treatment on Tuesday 14 March, finishing Friday 17 March. There have been no problems so far and she has suffered no side-effects, maintaining a healthy appetite throughout and enjoying use of the playroom. No further developments are expected until she has tests to assess the effect of this treatment during the first week of April at which time a further statement will be issued.

With the first course of Jaymee's chemotherapy complete, Peter Gravett set off for Switzerland, leaving Jaymee in the care of his colleague Nick Plowman. He had no idea that the medical conference he was going to attend would provide the turning point in the search for an alternative form of treatment for his famous new patient. The Swiss resort of Davos is as popular with the international conference circuit as it is with skiers. In winter, delegates can combine business with pleasure – hence its great attraction. From 18 to 26 March 1995, the subject being discussed in the huge conference centre on the mountain top was blood and bone marrow.

It was the 21st Annual Meeting of the European Group for Blood and Marrow Transplantation, and the world's most eminent experts on disorders of the blood were gathering to present and discuss their latest research. According to Peter Gravett, the very first meeting of the EBMT involved about ten people sitting in a bar in Austria, but as the years went by it grew and grew and now up to 1,400 delegates attend the meeting every year.

Because of its situation, the easiest way to get to Davos is to take the train which winds its way through spectacular scenery until it reaches the village high in the mountains. Peter Gravett was standing on the platform waiting for the train to arrive when he met two fellow bone marrow experts: Professor Grant Prentice, who runs the bone marrow transplant unit at the Royal Free Hospital in London, and Dr Steve Mackinnon, who used to work with Professor John Goldman at the Hammersmith but was now based in New York. They decided to travel together.

The journey to Davos takes two hours, and the conversation inevitably turned to Jaymee. It wasn't just the media who were interested in her case: there was intense curiosity among Peter Gravett's peers as well. In the space of just one week, their colleague had been catapulted on to the front page of every national newspaper in Britain.

But now he needed their help. Peter Gravett told them that the problem he faced was what to do next, assuming that he managed to get Jaymee's leukaemia into remission. It was obvious to Professor Prentice and Dr Mackinnon as well as to other colleagues with whom he discussed her case that week that Peter Gravett was reluctant to give Jaymee a second bone marrow transplant.

Although he knew that was what David wanted for his daughter and he had agreed to consider it, like Jaymee's original doctors, Peter Gravett had seen the statistics too and they painted a bleak picture. Apart from the relatively small chance of long-term survival, the risk in the transplant alone would be twice that of the first one. And the chance of her dying from the side-effects alone within several months of the transplant was as high as 80 per cent.

According to the International Bone Marrow Register, which keeps records of almost every bone marrow transplant in the world, there were only six children with relapsed leukaemia like Jaymee's who had been given second transplants. None had survived. There must be an alternative which would give Jaymee a better chance of good-quality life as well as the chance of long-term remission from her leukaemia.

Peter Gravett's two colleagues thought they had the answer. There was a new technique which was being tried in several centres of excellence around the world. They had both used it and Steve Mackinnon was presenting a paper on it at the conference. Gravett knew about the technique and had used it a couple of times; but as it was more commonly used for treating chronic, not acute, myeloid leukaemia, he had not considered it suitable for Jaymee.

Both Professor Prentice and Dr Mackinnon, however, thought it was worth a try, and when Peter Gravett heard about the results Mackinnon had achieved in New York, he began to take what his two colleagues were saying very seriously indeed.

The technique is called donor lymphocyte infusion and involves taking lymphocytes – a variety of white blood cells – from a compatible donor and injecting or 'infusing' them into the patient. The idea is that the donor's healthy cells will produce the same sort of effect as if the patient had been given a bone marrow transplant by producing the ammunition needed to help attack cancer cells.

Because it had only been tried in a small number of centres around the world, it was still classified as experimental, but there had been some notable success stories. In New York Dr Mackinnon had used the technique on twenty-two patients with chronic myeloid leukaemia who had relapsed after a bone marrow transplant and they had all gone into complete remission. At the Royal Free, Professor Prentice had used it on six patients and Professor Goldman had used it at Hammersmith Hospital too.

Most intriguing of all, it had even been tried on nine adult patients with relapsed leukaemia like Jaymee's at the Royal Marsden, where David Bowen had sought a second opinion for his daughter. In fact, the head of leukaemia research at the hospital, Professor Ray Powles, was writing a paper about them with one of his colleagues; but because no formal study had been established for children, the children's cancer specialists at the hospital had ruled it out for Jaymee.

For most of the second half of the journey to Davos, Peter Gravett and his two colleagues discussed in great detail the exact number of cells which should be given to Jaymee to achieve the best effect while minimizing the risks. The great advantage of the technique was that she would not have to spend weeks in hospital, as she would certainly have to do if she had another transplant. Donor lymphocyte infusion could be given on an outpatient basis every few weeks. Jaymee would simply need to come to hospital for the infusion and then go home again.

As soon as Peter Gravett arrived in Davos, it became immediately clear that donor lymphocyte infusion for acute leukaemia was beginning to excite a great deal of interest among the experts. There were several papers about the technique presented at the conference, and figures were given detailing the latest results from Europe. They showed that fifty-two patients with relapsed AML had so far been given donor lymphocyte infusion. Of those, eleven were still alive, the longest survivor still living three and a half years later. Most of the published research to date had been based on adults with chronic leukaemia, so these results were encouraging.

'Grant Prentice said that if he were me he would give Jaymee the lymphocytes,' Peter Gravett said. But there were enormous risks involved too. It was vital that he did not give Jaymee too many cells at once because if he did, they could engender a violent reaction which he might not be able to control, causing extensive damage to her internal organs and even killing her. On the other hand, if he gave her too few, the technique might not work at all. It was an extremely delicate balance in which the trick was to get a controlled reaction with the right number of cells, which was what Steve Mackinnon had been working on in New York – the importance of his work lying not in the type of leukaemia involved, but in the actual number of cells required to get a reaction. He told Peter Gravett how to calculate the exact number of cells he thought Jaymee should be given to ensure they did their job but without causing too much damage.

Grant Prentice and Steve Mackinnon were not the only people at Davos with whom Peter Gravett discussed Jaymee. John Goldman was there too, and so was Dr Jenny Treleaven, both close friends of Peter Gravett's, who had done most of the work on donor lymphocyte infusion at the Royal Marsden. Indeed, one of the first things which caught his eye as he arrived at the conference centre was a poster describing the way in which the technique was being used at the Royal Marsden.

All this, and the discussions he had at the conference, gave him renewed hope that there was a treatment he could offer Jaymee that would at least give her the chance of prolonged remission and good-quality life. On the face of it, this seemed to fulfil the criteria that Jaymee's own doctors had laid down for justifying further treatment.

In fact, one of those doctors, Simon Meller, was at Davos too. 'I met Jenny and Simon at a Swiss evening and had a long discussion with them and John Goldman about Jaymee,'

Peter Gravett said. 'We talked for ages after supper,' Simon Meller told me. Jenny told him more about donor lymphocyte infusion, reinforcing Gravett's conversation on the train. It was one of those evenings where, away from the formalities of the conference hall, everyone spoke frankly about what was at stake.

The Davos conference changed everything. From that point on, not only Dr Gravett, but NHS children's cancer specialists too, began to think differently about donor lymphocyte infusion and ask themselves whether it might be suitable for children like Jaymee after all. 'Literally three months earlier, it wouldn't even have been thought of,' Simon Meller said – three months which Jaymee did not have the luxury of waiting for. It was the end of March, and had it not been for David's determination, by now Jaymee would almost certainly have been dead.

Instead, she was still in the Portland Hospital recovering from her infection when Dr Gravett returned from Davos. There was still another week to go before he could test her bone marrow to see if the chemotherapy had worked. It would mean giving Jaymee another anaesthetic, but it was the only way of seeing how many leukaemia cells had been killed by the drugs.

When the day came David was nervous. He had been building up all his hopes over the last three weeks, relying on Jaymee's previous good response to drugs. When she was wheeled down to the operating theatre in the basement of the Portland Hospital, David was by her side. He stayed with her while she was given the anaesthetic and was in the operating theatre when Dr Gravett removed a sample of bone marrow from the spongy tissue at the base of her spine. It was all finished in ten minutes and Jaymee was wheeled out into the recovery room to regain consciousness.

Dr Gravett took the sample of Jaymee's bone marrow back

to his laboratory at the London Clinic to test it. On every other occasion when Jaymee had been given chemotherapy, her leukaemia had gone into remission after the first course. Would she do it again this time?

A few hours later, Peter Gravett told David the result. It wasn't what they'd been hoping for. The chemotherapy had killed only half the leukaemia. David was sanguine, however. He knew what Peter Gravett's strategy for Jaymee's treatment was now and he agreed with it. He would just have to be patient.

'I wasn't disappointed. I knew we'd got rid of half the leukaemia and that all we had to do now was get rid of the other half. She could have three more doses of chemotherapy if necessary. Many people need three or four doses before it works – it's just that, until then, Jaymee had responded every time to the first course.'

Since that first course of chemotherapy, which had had to be started quickly because time was running out, Dr Gravett had sent samples of Jaymee's blood and bone marrow to a special laboratory in Bath where cancer cells are 'grown' and injected with drugs to see which ones are most effective at killing them. It's a controversial procedure which has never been formally evaluated because there is only one place in the country which provides the service. But as far as Dr Gravett was concerned, Jaymee's leukaemia was now so drug-resistant after all the treatment she'd had over the last five years that any additional help he could get in devising the best cocktail of drugs was worth it.

He had been doing his own research too. There was another drug he wanted to give Jaymee which was only licensed for use on patients with breast or ovarian cancer but which was also being used in clinical trials as a way of overcoming drug-resistant cancer cells. It is called taxol and had been used on children with other types of cancer, but it was not licensed for use on children with AML (the type of leukaemia

Jaymee was suffering from). The risk was that it could affect the nerves in the hands and legs, causing all loss of sensation. Once he'd had the drug tests back from Bath, Peter Gravett was able to devise the cocktail of drugs, which included taxol, for Jaymee's second course of chemotherapy. He proposed to condense two doses into one concentrated over a period of thirty-six hours, during which Jaymee would be kept under sedation.

Everything was tailor-made to give Jaymee the best possible chance of success. But Peter Gravett was entering uncharted waters. There was no blueprint to follow for Jaymee's treatment, no accepted medical protocol, for most NHS children's cancer specialists would never have gone this far – from now on, Peter Gravett was virtually on his own. In the meantime, the media were desperate to know what he was going to do next.

On Tuesday 4 April he gave another press conference at the London Clinic. It was an extraordinary occasion, attended by reporters representing all the national and some international media organizations. Television and radio vans lined the street outside the clinic, and cables had been fed in through the first-floor windows to the room where the press conference was being held so that it could be broadcast live. On the desk in front of the place where Peter Gravett would sit, microphones were lined up waiting and the small room was packed with journalists.

All this for one anonymous ten-year-old girl known only as Child B. In her hospital bedroom at the Portland, Jaymee had no idea what was going on down the road and that the state of her health was attracting almost as much interest as the signing of a major international peace treaty.

At 9.15 a.m. Peter Gravett walked into the room, followed by Carolyn Meunier, who had organized the press conference. As he sat down, a reporter from Sky News wearing an earpiece asked him if he would mind waiting until they were broadcasting live before beginning to speak, such was the level of interest in what he had to say. Dr Gravett obliged and there was silence in the room until the reporter gave him the signal that he could start the press conference.

Child B was 'surprisingly well', he said, and had been allowed out to go to the park with her family. She had also been baking cakes in the hospital kitchen. The first dose of chemotherapy had got rid of only half the leukaemia, but he was planning to give her more after Easter. He had ruled out a second bone marrow transplant and now believed a new type of therapy called donor lymphocyte infusion was 'the best option'. Wasn't she just being used as a guinea pig? several reporters wanted to know. 'It would be possible to justify that description,' Dr Gravett replied, adding, 'It is also true to say that unless we were prepared to use new, promising techniques on patients who really have no other option, we would never be able to develop new methods of treatment.'

This was the question that lay at the heart of the controversy surrounding Jaymee's case. The need to promote advances in medicine within ethical limits while at the same time ensuring the most 'effective' use of public money might seem impossible to resolve to everyone's satisfaction; but once the story of Child B had achieved such national prominence, the problem itself could not be ducked. As the days went by and the debate continued, NHS managers and doctors alike could see for themselves that, whether they liked it or not, the questions raised by Jaymee's case were not going to go away.

There was something else Dr Gravett had to do before the Easter weekend, and it meant that for the first time since she had given Jaymee her bone marrow for the transplant, Charlotte would be the focus of attention. At the press conference, Dr Gravett had announced that she would be the donor for Jaymee's experimental treatment. The following day, there was a clear division between the tabloid newspapers and their broadsheet counterparts. 'Sister Gives Blood to Help Save Little B' was typical of the headlines in the tabloid press, while newspapers like the *Telegraph* ('Leukaemia Girl Facing Experimental Therapy') and *The Times* ('Experimental Therapy for Child B') were more measured in their assessment.

The following week Mike Robinson, the *Panorama* producer, and I met the Bowen family for the first time. It was the day before Charlotte was to donate the blood cells for Jaymee's treatment. The two sisters were sitting drawing in the playroom at the Portland Hospital. David had already told us that Jaymee was 'the boss'. If she didn't like us, she would tell us and that would be that. This was obviously someone who didn't suffer fools gladly so we were more than a little nervous as we set off in the lift for the fifth floor. Suddenly Child B was about to become transformed into a person and we had no idea what to expect.

Her face was turned away from us as we walked into the playroom, so our first sight of Jaymee was the back of her bald head. Then we saw her face and the enormous brown eyes. She didn't smile. Both she and Charlotte seemed subdued and withdrawn. After all, who were we but two more strangers her father had brought in? They were naturally suspicious. We stayed only a short time and explained that we were hoping to make a film about the treatment Dr Gravett was going to give Jaymee. It was as close to the truth as we were allowed to go because of the restriction imposed by the anonymity order. For the next five months, until David had told them the truth about Child B, we had always to be on our guard about what we said in front of Jaymee and Charlotte. All the questions we wanted to ask simply had to wait.

10

The Experiment Begins

The following morning, the Bowens arrived at the London Clinic where Charlotte was going to give blood for Jaymee's treatment. Whatever course of action Peter Gravett had decided on, it would have meant that, once again, Charlotte would be needed as a donor for her sister. In many ways, she was glad. For a brief interlude, she would be the centre of attention again and Jaymee would have to take second place.

But, like her sister, Charlotte had no idea how close to death Jaymee had been and she was surprised by what David said when he told her that she was going to have to give some cells to Jaymee. 'I said, "What's in it for me?" and Dad said, "Your sister's life." I said, "Oh, right."'

In January, when it had become obvious that Jaymee was ill again, Charlotte wanted to know what was going on, but no one would tell her. 'Everyone was rushing about and when I asked what was happening they would just say, "Not now, Charlotte, we've got better things to do, we've got to help your sister."'

'It's very difficult for Charlotte to see that Jaymee is getting so much attention without us being able to explain to her why she's getting that attention,' David admitted.

Now it was Charlotte's turn to help Jaymee again. But today *she* was the patient and it was Jaymee's turn to play the observer. Ossie had come with David so that he could look after Jaymee while David was with Charlotte. Everyone knew that, as with the bone marrow transplant, the process of removing the blood cells would be more distressing than giving them to Jaymee. Charlotte was going to have a tube inserted into her neck through which her blood would be filtered out through a sophisticated machine called a cell-separator. She was to be sedated while the tube was put in and throughout the time she was attached to the machine.

Earlier that day, Jaymee and Charlotte had another sisterly heart-to-heart. 'She said, "I don't care if you die,"' Charlotte told me. 'I said, "I bet you will." She said, "I bet I won't."'

But Jaymee was more concerned about her sister than she cared to admit. Although she didn't know quite how important Charlotte's cells could be, she knew that she was going to have to suffer on her behalf. 'No matter what they say, even if she's not feeling anything at the moment, she's going to feel it afterwards,' she said.

David, Ossie and Jaymee watched anxiously as an anaesthetist from Great Ormond Street Hospital gave Charlotte an injection and began to sedate her. It didn't work. When he tried to insert the tube into the side of her neck, Charlotte jumped violently, not in pain but in a reflex response to the touch of a needle in her neck, which clearly meant it was going to be difficult to get the tube in this way.

Standing at the end of the bed, Jaymee winced and her eyes filled with tears. She covered her face with her hands. It quickly became plain to everyone in the room that the only way to get the tube in was to do it under general anaesthetic. Charlotte was wheeled down to the operating theatre. Not wanting to leave her sister, Jaymee came too.

'I didn't want to watch, it was just something, some strange thing. You don't like looking at these things but you just want to watch and it was difficult because you've been through it before and it's painful.'

Jaymee wanted to stay in the operating theatre with Charlotte but she wasn't allowed to, so she left David with Charlotte and went to sit outside in the corridor with her eyes glued to the theatre's swing doors. Ossie sat beside her with his arm round her shoulder; but until Charlotte had emerged safely, it was obvious that nothing would comfort Jaymee.

It was one of those rare occasions where, although few words were spoken, it was clear that in times of crisis Jaymee and Charlotte try to support each other. It was one of the reasons David wanted Charlotte to spend as much time as possible with her sister – in case time really did run out. That morning, as he stood beside Charlotte in the operating theatre, David could only hope that the gamble he had taken in agreeing to more treatment for Jaymee would pay off and justify the distress he was having to put Charlotte through now. 'Any parent feels guilty if they watch their child going through anything painful. I certainly did. You know you've made the decision for the child and you're powerless now to do anything about it.'

Neither Charlotte nor Jaymee had any idea how important Charlotte's blood cells might be. David had to keep that to himself too. 'You are watching someone save someone's life,' he said. 'Charlotte doesn't really know that's what she's doing, she's just happy to help her sister out. She's not aware of the magnitude of what she's doing or why it's so necessary.'

When Charlotte came out of the operating theatre ten minutes later, Jaymee was still huddled on her chair clutching a teddy bear one of the nurses had brought her. 'All done now, she's all right,' David called to her.

'I knew she'd come out of it all right. I'd have killed the doctor if she hadn't,' Jaymee told me later. Charlotte was barely conscious as she was wheeled back to her room. Now she had to be connected to the machine which would filter out the lymphocytes which would be given to Jaymee. The process of extraction would take about three hours and would give Dr Gravett enough lymphocytes for at least four 'infusions'.

By giving Jaymee regular doses of these infection-fighting white blood cells, Dr Gravett hoped to kick-start her immune system so that it would be able to recognize new cancer cells and attack them. In fact, Jaymee's *own* immune system was non-existent. Whatever she now had in the way of an immune system was the product of Charlotte's bone marrow from the transplant the previous year. By giving Jaymee more of Charlotte's healthy cells, Dr Gravett hoped that they would recognize the remaining healthy bone marrow which was in Jaymee and make it work better.

As Charlotte came round, she seemed to be in pain, as well as being confused about why she had a tube in her neck which meant she had to keep still. No matter how hard the anaesthetist tried to convince Jaymee that Charlotte wasn't feeling anything, Jaymee wouldn't believe him. With her customary no-nonsense logic she asked why, if Charlotte wasn't in pain, she was moaning like that, and told him to get her sister a pain-killer.

Then Charlotte had to have a drip put into her wrist, through which her blood would be channelled back into her body. It caused her even more distress. Jaymee gently wrapped a bandage round her sister's arm and stroked it gently. After everything she had been through herself, she seemed to know instinctively how to comfort Charlotte. Peter Gravett noticed it too.

'I think the relationship with her sister is actually a very close one, although to see them together sometimes, one wonders!' he remarked. 'I think it's clear when there are times of stress that they do support each other. That sort of adversity really does bring them together.'

I asked Charlotte one day what life would be like if Jaymee

died. Without a moment's hesitation she replied, 'Like a living nightmare.' Apart from her obvious grief at losing Jaymee, it soon became clear that part of the reason for Charlotte's answer was a very real concern about how David would react to her if Jaymee died. 'He wouldn't be happy to see me,' she said. It revealed more than anything she had said before what it must be like to feel as if you are second best and how difficult it must be for parents facing the loss of a beloved child not to invest more love and attention in them than in the child they know will be left behind.

While Charlotte was hooked up to the cell-separator, David and Jaymee sat by her side, watching her blood as it went on its extraordinary journey from the tube in her neck, round the convoluted pathways of tubes in the machine which extracted the vital cells and collected them in a plastic bag, before making its way back into her body through the drip in her wrist.

Once Peter Gravett had collected enough cells, he took them to his laboratory where they were divided into separate bags ready for freezing. Then a sort of medical anti-freeze was added to stop the cells bursting as they were thawed. Finally, they were taken to the basement where they would be stored in liquid nitrogen at a temperature of $-180°C$ in the hospital's freezer until they were needed. Dr Gravett suspected that donor lymphocyte infusion would work best when it was given to patients whose cancer was in remission, so he planned to give Jaymee the first dose immediately after her second intensive course of chemotherapy in the hope that this second onslaught of drugs would kill off the rest of her leukaemia. It had to be done this way round, because if Jaymee had been given the chemotherapy after the lymphocytes, the drugs would have destroyed them too and all possible benefits would have been lost.

In spite of her discomfort, Charlotte was well enough to go

home at the end of that afternoon. The next day, the only sign of what she had been through was a small pinprick mark on her neck. But for those in the NHS who were more sceptical about embarking on medical experiments with children before a treatment had been successfully tested on adults, making Charlotte act as a donor when the chance of success was so small raised many questions.

'I think the publicity surrounding Jaymee's case has made a lot of doctors think about what is right and ethical to do, particularly the issue about what you can do to a healthy donor and what a healthy young donor might need to go through for a treatment which might not benefit the recipient,' said Dr Simon Meller – a question which he believed was even more difficult to resolve when Jaymee's chance of long-term survival was generally estimated to be no more than 10 per cent.

Although he never denied that he was to all intents and purposes using Jaymee as a guinea pig, Peter Gravett was equally certain that, provided he was careful and scientific in his approach, what he was doing was justified. 'I think if there's no other option, then you've got to decide whether there's any justification in treatment at all or whether you're simply going to stop,' he said. 'If you're not going to stop, then the logical thing to do is to go for what looks to be the best currently available treatment and sometimes that's an experimental protocol, especially in a situation where nothing has really worked very well in the past.'

But David knew now that, even though the chance of success was no more than 10 per cent, the treatment Dr Gravett was planning would buy Jaymee extra time, and whether it lasted six months or a year or even longer, it was infinitely better than what had been predicted in the middle of January. 'I think from Jaymee's point of view she's got a life now, and if the treatment fails or not she's got several months of good-quality life and it's been bought for her at a price I couldn't afford,' he said.

Three days later it was Good Friday – a day of rest for the whole family and one of the first days Jaymee had been away from hospital for a month. It was a relief for all of them to be away from the claustrophobic atmosphere of a hospital. It was a beautiful hot and sunny day, and the Bowens hired boats and went out on the Thames. David had bought sailor caps for Jaymee and Charlotte. They took it in turns to steer the boat, and when they weren't navigating they sat at the front and sunbathed. Ossie and Rita came too and the whole family seemed relaxed. At lunchtime they stopped for a picnic on the river bank and fed the ducks and munched lollipops sent from Harrods. It was difficult for all of them to believe that this was a day Jaymee had never been expected to see.

'It's difficult not to cry when you see your child and you know that she should technically be dead,' David said. 'Life was normal that day and it would be easy, as it is most of the time when she's happy, to ignore the fact that Jaymee is ill. I've got used to the fact that she's got no hair again, so to me she just looked perfectly normal feeding the ducks and play-ing with the swans and driving the boat around. It was a normal day that any parent would have with their children, only perhaps they're not aware of just how precious that day could be if circumstances changed.'

It was a perfect day and they had Easter weekend to look forward to. But the time away from hospital was all too brief. Four days later Jaymee would start her second dose of chemo-therapy under sedation. Dr Gravett said this would be the most effective way of giving high-dose chemotherapy over as short a time as possible, and Jaymee would be so sleepy that with any luck she would hardly notice what was happening. The day on the river had been a much-needed interlude, but in fact Jaymee's treatment had only just begun.

It was a familiar little procession which made its way up Devonshire Place to the London Clinic on Tuesday 18 April: David, smartly dressed as usual, accompanied by Jaymee and Charlotte arguing furiously. But Jaymee was in good spirits after her weekend off. Because they weren't used to treating children, the staff at the London Clinic had bought two sets of children's bed linen specially for Jaymee to make her feel at home in the hospital room that had been designed with adults in mind. Peter Gravett had also had to arrange for special dispensation from the local health authority before he was allowed to treat Jaymee there.

Like the seasoned hospital-goer that she was, Jaymee climbed on to the bed and settled down to play a game with her father while she waited for Peter Gravett to arrive and the chemotherapy to begin.

After Dr Gravett had examined Jaymee, he and David went outside into the corridor to discuss the possible side-effects Jaymee might suffer as a result of the drugs. One of the drugs he was going to give her had given her a fit while she was in the Royal Marsden having her bone marrow transplant the year before. David remembered it all too well. It had left him shaking and in tears and he had refused to leave her bedside or go to sleep in case it happened again. Fortunately, Jaymee had no recollection of it at all. She just wanted to get the chemotherapy over and done with so she could go home again.

'Jaymee is very confident in the team of people here,' David said that morning. 'She's just looking forward to getting out and is trying to nail Peter down to a time. She's worked out that at 2 a.m. Thursday morning she should be out of here and she's trying to see if she can convince Peter to let her go then. I don't think she's actually succeeding!'

It was typical of the businesslike manner in which Jaymee dealt with doctors and hospitals. It was all part of her survival strategy. As far as she was concerned, an attitude no doubt partly engendered by David, doctors were there to be questioned – not godlike figures to be obeyed at all times but fallible human beings capable of making mistakes. If they were going to give her drugs, she wanted to know what they would do to her.

'It's very important to trust your doctor, because if you don't trust your doctor then you could be putting yourself in danger,' she said to me one afternoon in hospital. When Peter Gravett had finished talking to David, David explained everything he had said to Jaymee. She listened carefully and then David signed the consent form agreeing to the treatment. It was a reminder of the responsibility he was taking for his daughter's life, but in the last two months he had read so much medical literature, and had had so many conversations with doctors, that he believed he now understood the risks as well as anyone.

'Peter and I talked for about an hour and a half today about the options for Jaymee's treatment,' David said later that day. 'We discussed what we can do and we know at what point we have run out of options. If there's something that he brings up that I'm not sure about, then we'll discuss it. If it's something I've heard about, I'll discuss it with him. And he is constantly in touch with additional doctors to tell them what he is planning for Jaymee and to ask if they have encountered any problems along the way. So it's a very equal relationship.'

Since the Davos conference, Peter Gravett had kept in close touch with Jenny Treleaven at the Royal Marsden and was following what was in effect the hospital's protocol for donor lymphocyte infusion. Over the following months he had long conversations with her about what he was doing, and if problems arose he would ask for her advice. It meant that although the NHS had no official involvement in Jaymee's treatment, it was very much supporting her behind the scenes.

Before Jaymee was sedated and the chemotherapy begun, she had to have an X-ray of her heart so that the effect of the drugs could be closely monitored. It is the heart which can suffer the most damage from successive doses of chemotherapy. Because the drugs are so toxic, they affect healthy organs in the body as well as attacking cancer cells. The more chemotherapy, the greater the chance of long-term damage. That was part of the risk involved in giving Jaymee yet another dose. It was certainly one of the reasons why her original doctors believed she'd had enough.

When the X-ray was over, Jaymee went back to her room and waited for the nurse to start giving her the drugs to sedate her. It didn't take long. Within half an hour she was curled up in bed with her eyes closed, her arm round Fred, her favourite teddy bear. Then a bag of saline solution was connected to her Hickman line to flush away any bacteria which might be growing inside it. When the bag had emptied, the first bag of chemotherapy drugs was connected to the valve at the end of the line. By now Jaymee was almost asleep and a hush fell over the room. The only sound was that of the syringe drive which released the cocktail of drugs drip by toxic drip. It was the start of a long thirty-six hours, during which David was not expecting to get much rest.

'I'll do what I normally do which is to sit up with her during the night, and I can go for thirty-six hours without any sleep. That's not a problem,' he said. Throughout that time, Jaymee was never left alone. Either David, Ossie or Rita would sit with her. In one of Jaymee's moments of semi-wakefulness, Rita gently stroked her hand and said, 'This is going to be our tough time.' Without a mother to comfort her, Rita's love and support were crucial to Jaymee at times like this. Lying in bed, she could see her grandmother's silver cross hanging like a beacon round her neck.

On the second evening, the whole family sat round

Jaymee's bed eating hamburgers. She had wanted to be awake for this, had made David promise that he would buy one for her too; but when he arrived back clutching the brown paper bags, she was fast asleep. She looked extraordinarily peaceful. The curtains were kept closed for much of the day because the bright light hurt Jaymee's eyes if she woke. At night, the lights were turned away from her. Time was marked by the regular changing of the drip bags.

Jaymee's calculations had been correct. At 2 a.m. on the Thursday morning it was all over, but despite her pleas she had to wait until morning before she was allowed to go home. Before she left, she had the strawberries she had ordered for breakfast. As before, however, the respite from hospital would be all too brief. Jaymee was due back in hospital two days later, when she was to have the first dose of Charlotte's cells.

11

A Taste of Tomatoes

It was Saturday 22 April, a day Peter Gravett had been waiting for with a mixture of excitement and nervousness. Ever since his discussions at Davos he had been calculating how best to give Jaymee the infusions of her sister's cells. He'd used the technique on just two other patients before, but they had chronic leukaemia, unlike Jaymee. One was a child whose leukaemia went into remission for seven months following the lymphocyte infusions, before he relapsed and died.

There was almost as much at stake for Dr Gravett as for Jaymee herself. 'I'm not nervous in the sense that we've done this before,' he said. 'I'm nervous in the long term in that of course I don't know what the chance of this manoeuvre actually being successful is, so although we know that there are a proportion of patients that initially respond, we actually don't know what the ultimate success rate is going to be and whether there will be late relapses. It's just that theoretically it should work once the donor cells start fighting the leukaemia cells.'

First, Dr Gravett had to collect the cells from the freezer in the basement. Charlotte went with him as she wanted to see where her blood had been stored all this time. Liquid nitrogen freezes anything with which it comes into contact, so Dr Gravett had to put on thick protective gloves before he opened the freezer. Clouds of vapour rushed out of the large tank as he reached in and pulled out two bags of Charlotte's frozen cells. They looked like packets of smoked salmon, pale orange with tiny veins running through them. Dr Gravett put them straight into the airtight container he had brought with him and then set off upstairs with Charlotte to the room where Jaymee and David were waiting. Time was of the essence now. It was important that the cells were thawed at the last minute and then given to Jaymee immediately.

Jaymee was looking decidedly fed up as Peter Gravett vanished into the bathroom and began thawing the bag of cells in the basin. 'Can you lot hurry up in there?' she called impatiently. Dr Gravett picked the bag out of the basin and held it up to the light to make sure the cells had thawed completely.

Then he was ready. The atmosphere in Jaymee's room was extraordinarily tense. David sat in a chair in the corner, watching intently as the doctor in whom he had placed all his trust emptied the bag of Charlotte's cells into four large syringes held by a nurse. Jaymee was lying on her side in the bed with the sheet pulled up round her neck. It made her skin look pale and her eyes even larger than usual.

'I'm always scared when I see something new because I don't know what it does and how it affects people, whether it's a cure, whether it's deadly. Things like that,' she said. No one else in the room that day knew the answer to those questions either. Now that the moment had come, all Peter Gravett could hope was that, between them, he and Steve Mackinnon had correctly calculated the precise number of cells to give Jaymee each time she was given an infusion, and that, somehow, they would produce the desired effect.

'Today's what all the rest of it has been building up to really,' he said. 'Ultimately, whether the lymphocytes work or not is going to determine whether the leukaemia comes back or not, so they're essential if we're to stand any chance of curing her. Whether she relapses again depends on all sorts of things; but if her new immune system manages to eradicate the leukaemia, then it should stay away without her needing further treatment.'

There was absolute silence in the room as the nurse picked up the first syringe, connected it to Jaymee's Hickman line and began slowly emptying the contents into it.

'Not only did I get pins and needles in my legs when they were giving it to me, it felt like I had pins and needles in my throat and in my chest. It felt like someone was squeezing me really tight and I wasn't getting any blood anywhere,' Jaymee said. Standing by her bed, Peter Gravett didn't take his eyes off her for an instant as Charlotte's cells made their way into her system. He knew that if things went wrong now it could be disastrous for them all. It was possible that Jaymee's body would have a violent reaction to the toxic anti-freeze in the cells, in which case her pulse could start racing and her blood pressure fall dramatically. If this happened, the infusion would have to stop at once.

Suddenly the room seemed to fill with a strange, sickly smell emanating from Jaymee. It was vaguely familiar but seemed out of place in this context. 'It tastes like tomato juice,' Jaymee told Peter Gravett. He laughed. So far so good. Apparently a smell of tomatoes or blackcurrants is a typical accompaniment to donor lymphocyte infusion. Unfortunately for Jaymee, the bad taste and the aura of tomato juice would probably last several days. It was making her feel sick and there were still three syringes to get into her that morning.

From his chair in the corner of the room David called, 'Are you all right, Jaymee?' 'Yes' came the reply of someone used to submitting to medical ordeals. Later that morning the telephone rang in Jaymee's room. It was Rita, anxious to know what had happened. Charlotte picked it up and with a great sense of importance told her grandmother, 'I've seen my cells, I've seen my cells!' 'They're making me feel sick,' Jaymee complained. 'It's only my blood,' Charlotte said, to which Jaymee replied icily, 'That's the point.'

None of Peter Gravett's worst fears had been realized that morning, and by mid-afternoon Jaymee was ready to go home. Until they knew whether the chemotherapy she'd been given earlier in the week had done its job, there was nothing anyone could do but wait.

All David and Peter Gravett knew was that if it hadn't worked, they'd be back to square one. Then the NHS children's cancer specialists who had been so critical behind the scenes would be able to say they had been right all along. Earlier that week Peter Gravett had been to a leukaemia lecture at the Medical Research Council at which he had sat and listened to the doctor who had devised Protocol 904, the regime which had been used on Jaymee, criticize the experimental nature of the treatment she was now being given.

It was medical politics in action, but there were serious issues involved too. It was what they perceived as the precariousness, the general lack of certainty about the outcome of this particular type of treatment that most concerned the NHS children's cancer specialists. Their view was that what they classified as one-off experiments on children were not ethical and would never be sanctioned by the NHS establishment.

'An ethical experiment in a child with relapsed leukaemia needs to be reasonably kind to the child and it needs to be a "good" experiment – in other words, one which the doctor involved thinks really might get somewhere,' said Simon Meller. 'It needs to be conducted not just on one child but in a planned way on a number of cases, so that at the end of the day you know for certain whether this treatment has a 1 per cent or 10 per cent chance of success.'

Underlying this argument was an essentially utilitarian approach to medicine. 'We shouldn't be doing things which are very unlikely to benefit the individual child unless the greater good of future generations of children with leukaemia is taken into account,' Dr Meller said. But if you are the parent of that individual child, where then should your priorities lie?

In Peter Gravett, David had found a doctor prepared to push forward the frontiers of medicine within what he believed were reasonable limits, and neither he nor Gravett could see what was wrong with this approach.

'I can understand that there are advantages to conducting studies in a controlled environment in an academic centre where all the data is being collected and properly analysed,' said Peter Gravett. 'I have a slightly different problem – which is how to give the best possible treatment for this particular little girl.'

12

Risks and Rationing

'You don't know what suffering is until you've been in hospital,' Jaymee told me the morning she was given her first dose of Charlotte's cells. 'Going to hospital sort of moulds itself on to you. You learn about medicines that you wouldn't know about unless you'd been in hospital. You learn how to do things you wouldn't know about unless you'd been in hospital.' And you learn about people who die? 'Yes, people you wouldn't normally care about unless you'd been in hospital.' Sobering words from a ten-year-old.

A week after Jaymee had been given the first dose of Charlotte's cells, she and David had just arrived home after spending a day at the London Clinic where Jaymee had been given an infusion of platelets to help restore her blood count, when her temperature began to rise. Realizing that she must have developed some kind of infection and not wanting to take any risks, David turned round and drove her straight back to London. It was late, and by the time they arrived at the Portland Hospital it was two o'clock on Saturday morning. A bag of antibiotics was immediately connected to Jaymee's Hickman line. It was a fungal infection, the result of the chemotherapy which had lowered her resistance to infections, and it was easily controlled by antibiotics, but it meant spending another six days in hospital. While she was there, Dr Gravett decided he would test Jaymee's bone marrow to see if the chemotherapy had worked and had succeeded in getting her leukaemia into remission.

It was late afternoon on 3 May when David helped to wheel Jaymee down to the basement of the Portland Hospital. Charlotte insisted on coming as well, but, much to her disappointment, she wasn't allowed further than the doors of the operating theatre. Jaymee was in good spirits; after all, she had no idea that this procedure was any more or less important than all the other times she'd been given an anaesthetic. But David knew. This time he waited outside in the corridor while Peter Gravett extracted the sample of bone marrow on which so much now depended.

David liked to be able to prepare himself for moments like this so that he could keep his emotions under control, but Peter Gravett had only decided to do the test that morning and it had taken him by surprise. As he paced up and down outside the operating theatre, occasionally peering through the little glass circle in the swing doors to look at his daughter lying unconscious on her side, David realized that in a few hours' time he would discover if the extraordinary gamble he had taken on Jaymee's behalf had any chance of succeeding. After the first dose of chemotherapy had failed to kill off all the cancer, David had reassured himself that the second course would do the trick because the drugs were more precisely tailored to her needs. But if that didn't work, he knew that all Peter Gravett would be able to offer Jaymee would be a few extra months of life rather than the chance of long-term survival. 'We're up against the wall – we're very nearly there,' David had said during Jaymee's thirty-six hours under sedation.

We were filming with David that day and I asked him then how he thought he'd react if Peter Gravett told him there was nothing more he could do for Jaymee. 'I think I would have to accept that, barring an act of God or a miracle, we'd gone to the limit of what modern science and technology could offer,' he said. 'We're at the leading edge of what's going on, and if Peter can't do anything about it and genuinely said, "I'm out of options, David," then I would be in a very difficult position.'

As we stood in the empty corridor waiting for Jaymee that afternoon, the magnitude of what was at stake seemed to hit him and tears suddenly rolled down his cheeks. 'She doesn't know how important a day it is for her,' he said. 'It would be awfully nice for Jaymee to go into remission and for me to know that from her having been written off she's now in there with a good chance,' he went on. 'I've gone through it a hundred times with Peter and he's very confident, but I won't be happy until I'm told, so I'll be trying my best not to show any emotions when Jaymee recovers consciousness.'

When Jaymee was wheeled out of the operating theatre ten minutes later, David followed anxiously as she was taken into the recovery room and stood waiting by her bed until she came round. Once she'd regained consciousness, Peter Gravett took the samples of bone marrow and set off back to his laboratory at the London Clinic to begin tests, leaving David with Jaymee at the Portland.

He expected to get the results within two or three hours. Everything now depended on the proportion of cancer or 'blast' cells in Jaymee's bone marrow. If they made up more than 5 per cent of the total, it would mean she wasn't in remission. There is an acceptable halfway house of between 5 and 10 per cent, but the official definition of remission is anything under 5 per cent of blast cells.

Peter Gravett had allowed us to film him as he got the result, a brave move in the circumstances because he had no idea which way it might go and whether he would have to answer a barrage of awkward questions if Jaymee hadn't gone into remission. The final stage of the testing procedure involved putting a slide smeared with a sample of bone marrow under a microscope and, with the help of a calculator, counting the different types of cell. As we stood in a small side room in the corner of his laboratory, nobody dared speak. The only sound was the tapping of the doctor's fingers on the calculator keys. It must have taken about a minute and a half to work out the result.

At last the tapping stopped and Peter Gravett looked up from his microscope. The normally reserved doctor was smiling broadly. 'Three per cent,' he announced. 'She's officially in remission.'

It was something Jaymee's original doctors had believed was almost impossible. In her affidavit to the High Court, Valerie Broadbent, her doctor at Addenbrooke's, had said: 'A complete remission is unlikely to be achieved.' Now, more than three months later, Jaymee had defied the odds.

Delighted though he was, Peter Gravett was careful to keep the nature of this achievement in perspective. 'The treatment so far has worked, but the difficult bit is making sure the leukaemia doesn't come back and without any further treatment it would be back very quickly. What we don't know is whether this donor lymphocyte programme is capable of actually getting rid of those last few cells, but this is the ideal situation to be starting from. If there are too many leukaemia cells around, the lymphocytes just can't cope; but now that they're down below 5 per cent, there's a more realistic chance of being able to control the rest of the leukaemia.'

That was the problem. Even though Jaymee was officially in remission, there were still cancer cells lurking in her blood. The trick now was to make sure the lymphocytes attacked them before they multiplied.

But before anyone worried about that, Peter Gravett had an important telephone call to make. He dialled the number of the Portland Hospital and asked to be put through to David Bowen. David listened carefully to what he was told and then said quietly, 'Thank you very much.'

'When I got the phone call I was standing at the nurses' station in the corridor because they thought it was better for me to take the call out there,' David said when we saw him an hour later. 'As I walked down the corridor to the phone, the sister in charge gave me the thumbs up and then I think I was in pieces. I felt euphoric.'

As we stepped out of the lift, Charlotte came rushing towards us. 'Jaymee's blood's clear, Jaymee's blood's clear,' she said with enormous excitement, grinning from ear to ear. Was David really right when he told us that neither of his daughters 'had a clue' why this moment was so important?

In her bedroom, Jaymee was lying on her bed watching a video and munching a McDonald's. She appeared to be entirely oblivious to the merriment going on around her. Rita and Ossie were there; so were her two cousins, Rochelle and Nadine. Everyone was smiling. Even Jaymee allowed the occasional grin to turn up the corners of her mouth.

'She's just happy that as far as she's concerned she doesn't need any more chemotherapy and that marks the start of her physically spending a lot of time out of hospital,' David said. 'She's now going to be technically an out-patient so she can go back to school and enjoy herself like any other child would do and come to hospital every so often for the lymphocytes.'

Two days later, Scaltback School welcomed back its most famous pupil. It was four months since she'd been to school, and when her teachers had seen her in January they believed it would be for the last time. They were amazed to see her looking so well. 'We didn't expect to see her back at all,' said David Pugh. 'The fact that she is back is a delight to everyone.' Watching Jaymee as she sat among the other pupils, it was difficult to believe she had ever been away, let alone been on the point of dying.

In her customary businesslike manner she attended all her lessons and chatted to her friends. Halfway through the morning, David crept round the outside of the building and peeped into Jaymee's classroom so that he could see for himself the image he believed he would never see again. There she was, sitting at a desk surrounded by her classmates, with only her bald head to distinguish her from the other children.

'I've never been drunk, but I suppose it's a feeling similar to that, a really nice sort of high,' he said. 'You know she's walking into school and she shouldn't technically have been there – it's hard to describe.'

It was a strange day for staff and pupils too, for they all knew what Jaymee officially did not – that she was the Child B whose story had been on the front pages of every newspaper in the land. No one was allowed to say anything, but Jaymee's teachers couldn't help wondering when someone would, inadvertently, let the cat out of the bag.

The following day, the *Daily Mirror* published a photograph of Jaymee taken from behind with her head blanked out by black squares. 'Little B Back at School' read the headline. The identity of the little girl in the white shirt, short white socks and long dark skirt would have been obvious to anyone who knew her, but Jaymee was still officially protected by the anonymity order imposed at David's request. Until he believed that her treatment was really working, that was the way he wanted it to stay. In the meantime, as far as he was concerned, headlines like that could only vindicate the battle he had fought against the NHS.

'Jaymee deserved another chance; and if she takes that chance and it pans out for her, then that's fine. If she takes the chance and it doesn't pan out, then at least she will have been given it, which is better than not being given it at all. That's all I wanted,' David said.

From now until the end of the summer term, Jaymee spent an average of two days a week at school, and within a short space of time she had caught up with the four months of lessons she had missed. 'Jaymee just copes,' Charlotte told me somewhat wistfully. 'With everything.'

A week after her return to school, Jaymee went back to hospital for the second dose of donor lymphocytes. Peter Gravett had taken enough for four doses because he knew it might take some time to generate the reaction he was hoping for. It was called graft-versus-leukaemia effect and it would mean that Charlotte's cells were actively fighting off any new or remaining cancer cells in Jaymee's blood. The physical evidence was likely to be a rash on her skin or white spots in her mouth, but there had been no signs after the first dose of cells.

The risk Peter Gravett had taken in giving Jaymee this treatment was that in order for her to experience the positive effects of the cells she would also need to develop a response called graft-versus-host disease. This meant that as well as doing their job in attacking the leukaemia, Charlotte's cells were also attacking their 'host' – in other words, Jaymee. This reaction had to be kept under control – if allowed to go too far it could kill her – and it was for this reason that Dr Gravett had been so anxious to calculate the precise number of cells to give Jaymee in each dose. Too few and there would be no positive effects. Too many and she could die what her original doctors knew only too well was a horrible death in which the donor cells could literally destroy the person they intended to save.

'You can lose the surface of the skin over almost the entire body,' said Professor Ross Pinkerton. 'The cells can also act against the liver and against the bowel, which produces diarrhoea, abdominal pain and dehydration. Graft-versus-host disease can certainly kill you, and we've had a number of children over the last few years who've had bone marrow transplants where this has been the cause of death. I read somewhere earlier in this controversy that dying from leukaemia was no worse than dying from the side-effects of experimental treatment – and this is simply not the case.'

It was because he had seen children die in such agony from graft-versus-host disease that Professor Pinkerton had refused to countenance putting Jaymee through experimental treatment which hadn't already been thoroughly tested on adults. Adults could agree to be guinea-pigs in the full knowledge that the experiment could go wrong. Children could not. That was why he and other children's cancer specialists were prepared to be accused of being over-cautious.

Both Peter Gravett and David knew the risks and believed they had done everything they could to avoid a crisis, but their critics also wondered what David's response would be if Jaymee did develop uncontrollable graft-versus-host disease. Then what would he have to say to the doctor in whom he had placed so much trust? And what would the public think of the father who had deprived his daughter of a dignified death?

As well as the medical politics involved in the case of Child B, there was genuine anguish being expressed by doctors who had seen children die from the ravages of experimental treatment – deaths which David could not possibly imagine.

This was where the real battleground between David Bowen and the NHS children's doctors lay. *He* believed Jaymee had the right to be treated even if her chances of survival were almost non-existent. *They* believed the knowledge they had acquired through years of medical practice gave them the right to say no.

'What makes me angry about the Child B case is that the cost came into it,' said Simon Meller. 'But the real cost was not pounds, shillings and pence; the real cost that everyone was talking about, the sort of hidden agenda, was of course the emotional and psychological cost to the child. That's what the doctors disagreed about.'

While these arguments continued to divide leukaemia specialists, Jaymee herself seemed remarkably well. It was now the end of May and she was fit enough to join her classmates on a day trip to France, an unexpected bonus and something she had hardly dared look forward to in case she was too ill to go. It was a long and tiring day for her, but it symbolized a return to the normality she had not experienced for so long. Just being with her friends, crossing the Channel on a ferry, playing on the beach, gossiping on the coach – all these things were rare treats for a girl who had spent so much of her life in hospital.

Coinciding with this trip was the launch of an important but little-publicized document by Cambridge Health Authority and a public meeting which placed Jaymee's case firmly in the context of healthcare rationing. The document was called *Challenging Choices* and was written by Dr Ron Zimmern, the man who had taken the decision not to fund a second transplant for Jaymee. 'Rationing is an entirely necessary and legitimate activity,' he said in the foreword to the document. If it hadn't been obvious before that the decision not to pay for Jaymee's treatment had been made, at least in part, in this context, it certainly was now. And it was obvious that, as far as Dr Zimmern was concerned, the sooner the public faced up to what was happening, the better.

'The reason why we're faced with this dilemma of having to make choices is because there is a mismatch between the resources that are available to us and the demands and expectations of our patients, and this mismatch has certain consequences,' Dr Zimmern told the meeting. In other words, some people would have to go without. 'Necessary sacrifices' would have to be made, he said, if the finite amount of money given to the NHS was to be put to the most equitable use. And what that meant in practical terms was that much tougher decisions would have to be made about which types of treatment were most effective. In his document, Dr Zimmern spoke of the clash of two philosophies – the utilitarian ethic, which promoted the greatest happiness of the greatest number (and which Jaymee's NHS doctors had already wrestled with on the question of experimentation); and the Kantian ethic, which placed individual need beyond all other considerations. Weighty stuff indeed for a document which was supposed to be aimed at explaining to the general public why their health authority might feel obliged to refuse them treatment. But it was quickly becoming clear that Cambridge was no ordinary health authority.

When Dr Zimmern paused for questions, the obvious one was asked immediately. Did he still think he made the right decision about Child B? By then it was well known that Jaymee's leukaemia was in remission, but Dr Zimmern's answer was unequivocal. The point about the Child B decision was not whether it was right or wrong but whether it was legitimate, he replied. The Health Authority had to be seen to have considered 'all the relevant factors and not to have considered irrelevant factors such as the colour of Child B's hair or anything like that'. An unfortunate statement given that at that particular time Jaymee had no hair at all.

But there were serious issues here, and both Ron Zimmern and Stephen Thornton, the Health Authority's chief executive, wanted to tackle them head-on and have continued to do so ever since. They believed that if rationing was to become an explicit part of the NHS as opposed to taking place behind closed doors, then not only did the public have a right to know, but health authorities had a duty to discuss it.

'Some doctors and managers have been very frightened of the implications of being caught in the media maelstrom, and it's leading to defensive behaviour in some quarters,' Mr Thornton told me later. 'I've had colleagues from other health authorities tell me very honestly that they would have paid [for Jaymee's treatment] even though they thought it was the wrong thing to do.'

The stance he took over Jaymee's case won him plaudits from the highest echelons of the National Health Service's Management Executive as well as from the then Health Secretary, Virginia Bottomley. This was hardly surprising. Although Stephen Thornton had shown remarkable courage by daring to go where most health authority managers feared to tread, as far as the Department of Health was concerned he had done them a favour by saying things which would be instant vote-losers if uttered by ministers.

As for David, had Ron Zimmern handled him more diplomatically, he says he might have accepted the Health Authority's stance. 'His first mistake was to say we don't talk to parents. You're in very grave danger when you're dealing with a parent in an explosive situation like this, in which the life of a child is at risk, of pushing that parent over the edge. You can achieve anything you want if you do it right. His problem was how he dealt with me.'

Many months later, when I was able to talk to Jaymee about Child B, she said simply, 'I think they should have come and met me and seen what I was like because meeting the child can sometimes change people's minds.'

I asked her what the Health Authority managers would have seen if they'd come to meet her. 'Well, what I would have thought they would have seen was a child that needs help, because otherwise if you refuse one child then other parents are going to get worried that they're going to refuse their child.'

Presumably that was precisely the reason why Ron Zimmern refused to get involved in discussions with individual parents. The risk of Kant beating the utilitarians might have been just too great.

13

Breakthrough

On 30 May, a week after the health authority meeting and Jaymee's trip to France, she was given the third dose of Charlotte's cells. There was still no sign of them working and Jaymee seemed depressed and tired when she arrived at the London Clinic. She didn't enjoy the fortnightly infusions which gave her a bad taste in her mouth and made her smell of tomatoes for two days – particularly as nothing seemed to be happening. 'There were times when I just felt like giving up,' she said later.

By now, Peter Gravett was starting to get anxious too. After today there would only be one dose of cells left. 'It would be reassuring to see some sort of evidence of a reaction at this stage, but everything's completely normal,' he said. 'No signs of any skin rashes; all the things that we look for are negative.'

Without any of the signs of graft-versus-host disease, it was impossible to tell if Charlotte's cells were having the positive effects they were hoping for either, and without them Jaymee's leukaemia was likely to relapse very quickly. The longer it took for the cells to work, the more likely it was that this would happen, and Peter Gravett believed they would have a better chance of working if Jaymee was in remission. The problem he faced if she relapsed was that giving her more chemotherapy would destroy the lymphocytes altogether. It was a situation he was desperately trying to avoid, and there were times over the next few weeks when he seemed to be performing a precarious juggling act.

To try to stimulate Charlotte's cells, he started giving Jaymee a drug called Interferon, which David could inject her with at home twice a week. The injections were painful but caused few side-effects apart from mild flu-like symptoms. Peter Gravett was pulling out every stop which medical science could offer to help his patient. He knew that, as each day passed, time was becoming more precious for the girl whose luck had officially run out four months earlier.

David knew too, and was determined to make the most of it. At the end of the half-term week, he took Jaymee, Charlotte and James to a fair near Ossie and Rita's house. Jaymee wore a floppy denim hat with lace round the edges which almost completely covered her bald head and neck. Nobody stared, nobody knew that the girl striding across the fairground at sunset eating candyfloss or driving the dodgems with such alacrity was the Child B they'd read about. That night, Jaymee's eyes were smiling. David stood watching his daughter as she spun round in a giant plastic tea cup, waving as she passed. Only those who knew the secret understood quite how valuable moments like this could be.

A fortnight later, Peter Gravett made the now familiar trip to the basement of the London Clinic and removed the last two bags of Charlotte's cells from the freezer. It was seven weeks since he'd given Jaymee the first dose and there was still no sign of a response. 'It's such an unpredictable situation,' he said that day. 'She could relapse next week or next year – the length of remission after chemotherapy is variable.'

Now both he and David had to face the possibility that they would need to take more cells from Charlotte. It was not a prospect either of them relished and, as far as the NHS children's cancer specialists were concerned, it raised questions about the rights of children as donors as well as questions about how far doctors should go in chasing what some of them believed were diminishing returns for the patient.

'We don't give up any more than the families do,' said Professor Ross Pinkerton, 'but you reach a stage where you have to look at the child and just say, "Is what we're doing in this child's interests, or are we just risking going on and on and on until the child eventually dies?" And then with hindsight you think that child could have had a few months with their friends and their family. It's always easier to opt for the more treatment option. The difficult decision is to work through with the family why you don't feel more treatment is appropriate.'

Peter Gravett hadn't yet reached that point. Jaymee was still in remission, her blood count was normal and she seemed reasonably well. Why stop now? David agreed. 'I watch Jaymee on a daily basis and I can see that she's her normal self. I'm quite happy that so long as she comes to hospital once a week and then spends the rest of the time enjoying herself, going to school, playing and doing things that she wants to do, then it's worth it.'

But the strain of the last few months was beginning to show. David couldn't sleep. 'I'm having a lot of trouble lately, I can't grasp why. I physically have to force myself to go to sleep and it's usually in the early hours of the morning. I sit there thinking, What am I going to do next? When do I as a parent have to say, "Enough is enough"?'

Together, David and Peter Gravett decided to wait another three weeks before taking any more cells from Charlotte. That would give them enough time to see whether the Interferon would kick-start the cells Jaymee had already been given before putting Charlotte through the ordeal of yet another general anaesthetic.

Unlike adults, children have no legal right to refuse to be

donors, and Jaymee's story prompted calls not only by some doctors but also by lawyers, for specific protection for children like Charlotte. In an article entitled 'Child bone marrow donors – victims or volunteers?' published in July 1995 in the journal *Family Law*, the author, a senior law lecturer at Manchester Metropolitan University, wrote: 'No child should be presumed to make himself or herself available in medical procedures merely to promote the welfare of another.' Highlighting the potential psychological dangers, the article inquired: 'To what extent can the child be persuaded that he or she has an emotional stake in helping the recipient of the bone marrow? To what extent does the child fear parental disapproval if he or she fails to cooperate?'

But how difficult it would be to refuse if you knew that your sister's life depended on your blood, and how much more difficult if you were only partly aware of why it was you were being asked to give it.

Three weeks later, on 3 July, Charlotte found herself back in the London Clinic preparing for another anaesthetic. Another tube was inserted into her neck and she was hooked up to the cell-separator again. This time, Jaymee didn't wait outside the operating theatre. She couldn't bear to watch. Instead she lay down on her bed and went to sleep. That way it would all be over more quickly.

'Charlotte's volunteering without knowing the real significance of what she's doing,' David said. 'She's actually saving her sister's life and I think if I could tell her that, it would make it a lot better for her.'

When Charlotte recovered consciousness she seemed to be in even more distress than the previous time. As he watched his daughters lying in the hospital beds at opposite ends of the room, David, as usual, tried to conceal his emotions. 'I was concerned for Charlotte because of the pain, but also for Jaymee because I could see it in her face that she was concerned and they were both looking to me and in fact there was little I could do,' he said.

Yet David had given his consent for both of them. That was the gamble he had taken and the responsibility he had to bear, and that same morning, after weeks of waiting, he discovered that it had been worthwhile. Jaymee had been complaining about a sore throat for the last two weeks, so when she had arrived at the hospital with Charlotte, Dr Gravett examined her mouth. As soon as he shone a light into it he could see the tell-tale signs of graft-versus-host disease he had been waiting for: little white spots and an inflammation at the back of her throat, and her lips were bright pink. It had taken ten weeks, but at last Charlotte's cells were starting to do their job. That was why Peter Gravett had decided to go ahead and take some more that day.

'Because we had some difficulty starting up the graft-versus-host disease in the first place, if I now give her no more provocation – in other words, any more of Charlotte's cells – and I don't give her any more Interferon, then there is just as much danger that the whole thing will fizzle out as there is that it's going to get out of control,' he said. As soon as Charlotte had finished donating the fresh cells, Peter Gravett gave Jaymee another dose. The next few weeks would be crucial, but David was delighted.

'From my viewpoint it's brilliant, because it means that she's on the best possible course. If I could have put her anywhere, I would have wanted her right where she sits at the moment.'

The daughter in whom he had placed so much faith had more than vindicated her father's struggle to get her treated. That was as much the cause of David's pleasure as anything else. 'I try to make the best decisions for her based on the facts that I have in front of me. I knew that if she could cope with the chemotherapy, she would be fine. And she sailed through that, went into remission and now she's sailed through this and got graft-versus-host disease. There's little else I can ask of her. She's done me very very proud,' he said that day.

As for Jaymee, she knew that whatever it was she had in her mouth might be a good thing as far as her father and doctor were concerned, but it was also very painful. 'It was horrible. I got this huge big rash in my mouth. I thought it might be an ulcer, but then it spread and it was getting hard to open my mouth and eat and swallow.' There are four levels of graft-versus-host disease, and Jaymee was at level two – perfect as long as Dr Gravett could keep it under control.

'They say I've reached halfway. I'm not sure quite what to expect,' Jaymee said. 'I feel quite good within myself, a lot better than a few months ago,' she added. But today was another important milestone in Jaymee's treatment. The fact that she'd developed graft-versus-host disease meant that her chance of long-term remission from leukaemia had increased significantly – from around 10 per cent to as much as 30 per cent.

'Once Jaymee went into remission we knew it would be all right,' David said. 'Jaymee would pull through. We knew she was going to have a good run for her money and that if anybody should make it, it was her. She has that guardian angel watching over her and we knew that if everything went to plan she would be fine.'

Peter Gravett, too, was delighted with the progress Jaymee had made. 'I think Jaymee has been rather dispirited at the sheer length of time that it's taken to get on top of it, but I think she's also beginning to feel that maybe there's light at the end of the tunnel now. When we started off treatment she was really very reticent about what was going to happen to her, and over the months she's become more confident, not just about the hospital and the people who are treating her now but also about her own future. She's looking ahead to what's going to happen in the months and years to come.'

But perhaps most important, as far as Jaymee was concerned, was the appearance of a thin black layer of hair on her head. She knew that once her hair began growing in earnest, it wouldn't be long before she looked normal again. That was the kind of milestone *she* liked.

Just over a month later, on 5 August, Jaymee celebrated her eleventh birthday, the day no one had expected she would live to see. It was a beautiful, hot Saturday, and Ossie and Rita had planned a birthday party in their back garden. Rita had been cooking for several days beforehand. She wanted everything to be perfect. Tables were brought out into the garden and filled with food. Smoke from the barbecue, where Rose Sunter, David's lawyer, was cooking vast amounts of chicken and sausages, wafted through the garden.

There was live music too. Ossie's cousin had a steel band which they set up in the garden. Everyone wanted to try and play the drums.

Jaymee looked lovely. Her hair was now thick enough to cover all of her head and its darkness offset her large brown eyes. She wore an outfit she had chosen on a trip to Harrods earlier that week, given to her as a birthday present by its chairman, Mohammed Al-Fayed. The black net skirt and white blouse with frills at the cuffs made her skin look even darker than usual. The pale, gaunt figure we had first encountered nearly four months earlier genuinely seemed to have vanished, to be replaced by a striking eleven-year-old girl with dimples in her cheeks and a mischievous smile.

'It hadn't occurred to me that I would be at her eleventh birthday party,' David said. 'I was mentally preparing myself for the possibility that she wasn't going to be there, so I think Jaymee's eleventh birthday will probably be one of the most important days in my life.'

Whatever lay ahead for Jaymee, that day was a triumph for the Bowen family, a milestone whose significance no one could deny. The man who had made it possible had been invited to be the guest of honour at this most important of birthday parties and to help hold the knife as she cut the cake. For this was Peter Gravett's celebration as much as Jaymee and David's. Ever since he had agreed to take Jaymee on, he had known that if the chemotherapy had failed or the experimental treatment had gone horribly wrong, the NHS children's cancer specialists – one of whom had gone so far as to accuse him behind his back of 'piddling about with charitable funds' – would have been ready to shake their heads and say, 'We told you so.' And he knew they would have been justified.

He also knew that had he been working in the NHS he would never have been allowed to do what he had done for Jaymee. The ethical constraints would have been too strict. He'd taken a gamble and it had paid off, but it could just as easily have gone the other way. When it came to children, the NHS did not allow that sort of gambling. The costs were too high. It was just that when he'd first seen Jaymee, Peter Gravett hadn't had the heart to say no to a girl he instinctively felt wasn't ready to give up on life.

As the steel band started to play 'Happy Birthday' in a wonderful calypso beat, he was standing behind Jaymee as she plunged the knife into the large pink-and-white cake. Everyone was smiling as the song was played over and over again, each time more jubilantly. Then the dancing began. Ossie put his arms round Jaymee's shoulders and they swayed gently to the music. Charlotte, together with Rochelle and Nadine, bounced exuberantly up and down under a tree. In the corner of the garden Rita danced with a friend. In the middle of it all was Rose Sunter, her dress fanning out around her as she twirled one of the children round and round.

But David didn't join in. He sat in a chair watching Jaymee, his eyes shielded by dark glasses. Even on this day, his emotions were kept firmly in check.

The song seemed to last for ever. As everyone sang 'Happy Birthday, dear Jaymee', a bubble of laughter would escape from her mouth and her smile spread from ear to ear. Whatever happened now, it had been worthwhile. When I asked Jaymee later which she could remember as the best days of 1995, she replied without hesitation, 'My birthday. I remember that as a very happy day.'

It was almost time to tell her the truth about Child B.

14

'Never Give Up'

Two days before Jaymee went back to school for the start of the autumn term, she and David went for a walk in the park. Provided she was well enough to know, he'd always planned to tell her the truth about the last eight months before she went back to school – just in case someone else did. But when it came to the moment, it wasn't easy to know what to say. They sat side by side on the swings while David summoned up the courage to begin.

'I'd tried to pave some of the way before I spoke to her, but it was still a very difficult thing to do,' he told me a few days later. 'I sat her on the swing next to me and it took me about twenty minutes to be able to actually start the conversation.'

'He told me everything,' Jaymee said. 'Everything that had been happening with the court case, the Health Authority, everything. I thought, Why didn't you tell me before?'

'She didn't explode or anything,' said David. 'She's the sort of child that asks intelligent questions and probing questions and that's basically what she did. She asked me why they didn't think it was worthwhile treating her. She said she felt doctors should treat all children and she said, "Did they give you a reason why they wouldn't treat me or why they felt the odds weren't worthwhile?" and I said, "No. They just said it wasn't worthwhile and so we went to court about it."'

The one thing David wanted to conceal from Jaymee was the exact chance of survival she had been given by her original doctors, although she was to find out soon enough. But after that conversation she realized she could have died, and she was torn between understanding why David had wanted to hide the truth from her and anger that in doing so he might also have deprived her of the opportunity of putting her emotional affairs in order. 'You'd like to know if your life was going to end in eight days or twenty-four hours so you could make the most of it,' she said. 'You'd want to know so you could say your goodbyes.'

It was only now, five months after our first meeting with Jaymee, that we could talk openly about what had happened to her during that time. Until David had told her the truth, we too were sworn to secrecy.

When Jaymee and I talked subsequently about David's decision to keep her in the dark, there were many times when she would say that her opinion was that children 'have the right to be told everything'. It also became clear that there were times when she had wondered how ill she really was. 'I thought if there was anything serious going on then he would tell me, but obviously I was wrong about that,' she said, adding, as only Jaymee knows how, 'I know he was doing it with my best interests at heart, so I won't put that to him.'

At other times, Jaymee was ambivalent about whether she would have preferred to know the truth at the time. 'Are you glad he didn't tell you?' I asked one day. 'Yes,' she said at once. But if I asked her another day, her answer would be different.

Now he had told Jaymee the truth, David felt it was time to ask the court to lift the order protecting her identity. It had been imposed to shield her from the knowledge of how ill she was, and now she knew it seemed to serve no useful purpose. There was another reason too. Several weeks earlier, the firm of solicitors acting for the anonymous donor had written to David telling him that the donor was no longer prepared to continue funding Jaymee's treatment. They considered it should now be up to the NHS to take her back.

But it wasn't that simple. At the beginning of September, Cambridge Health Authority agreed to pay the cost of what they described as the 'routine monitoring' Jaymee was being given by Dr Gravett – in other words, the regular blood tests and other checks that anyone who had been given a bone marrow transplant would need. What they were not prepared to pay for, however, was the cost of any 'experimental' treatment, by which they meant either another transplant or the donor lymphocyte infusions which appeared to be keeping Jaymee's leukaemia in remission.

David wanted to be in a position to pay the bills for Jaymee's treatment if she relapsed again. Peter Gravett had told him it was perfectly possible to give her more of Charlotte's cells. But if the Health Authority refused to pay, where would the money come from? David believed it would be easier to raise money for further treatment if Jaymee's identity was revealed. He wanted to have the option of appealing to the public for help since it would obviously be pointless taking the Health Authority to court again.

On Wednesday 25 October, David's request to have the anonymity order lifted was heard by three Appeal Court judges, none of whom was in favour of publicity for its own sake, but who agreed that it should be up to the father of Child B to decide what was in her best interests. He had responsibilities towards her shared by no one else. Furthermore, they said, the courts should not be in the position of denying her access to funds for her treatment.

Just after midday, the anonymity order which had protected Jaymee for seven months was lifted. An hour later, the BBC's *One o'Clock News* led its half-hour bulletin with the first pictures of Child B. From that moment, 'Little B' became Jaymee Bowen, the girl who never gave up.

Jaymee had recorded her interview a month before – five days after David had told her the truth about her illness. It was a Saturday afternoon and she seemed relaxed and confident as we sat down at opposite ends of a sofa. By now she was so used to having the camera around that she hardly seemed to notice it.

'I say never give up unless you are' – Jaymee pinched the air with her fingers – 'unless you are just on the last little drop of life you have in you. Never give up. Because if you give up you will just end up with nothing left.' Her words reverberated around the room. Nobody breathed. It was the first time we'd seen her since her conversation with David and we had no idea what she was going to say.

We talked about the reason why her NHS doctors hadn't wanted to go on treating her because of their reluctance to see her suffer any more. Without hesitating she replied, 'Well, I'd rather have gone through more suffering to live than not go through anything and die.'

'Do you think if you'd known that at the time that's what you would have said?' I asked.

'I would have said exactly the same thing.'

'Even if the treatment was painful and even if it took a long time?'

Jaymee nodded.

'Even if you had to spend a long time in hospital?'

She looked up with a weary expression on her face. 'I've spent long enough in hospital, it can't get much longer.'

'And you're prepared to spend more, or whatever it takes?'

Again she nodded.

I wondered if there were some children who wouldn't be prepared to go through that.

'Of course there are *some* children who wouldn't do that,' Jaymee said, jabbing her little finger into her cheek. 'But I'm not one of them.'

It was an extraordinary performance. The combination of physical and emotional suffering that Jaymee had endured over the last six years seemed to put her into a class of her own. When Jaymee's teachers saw the programme they found it difficult to recognize the person they thought they knew so well. There was a toughness in her words and an edge to her voice, an arrogance even, which none of them had heard before.

There was a question I was curious to know the answer to, given that David had explained the reason why he had gone to court in the first place. What would she say to the Chief Executive of Cambridge Health Authority, I asked, if he was sitting in front of her?

Jaymee's eyes narrowed. 'Well, I wouldn't just sit there, I'd just go over there and whack him one,' she said.

'And then what would you say?'

'Thank you for nothing. Because now look at me. I'm fine. You could have paid for it. You had the chance and you blew it.'

The following day, Jaymee's words and her remarkable story were the main item in almost every national newspaper, her determination and zest for life captured by a photograph taken on the evening she went to the fair. Her head, covered by the floppy denim hat, was turned towards the camera, her eyes sparkling and defiant. It was the image which captured Jaymee at her best. Tabloid and broadsheet papers alike paid tribute to her courage and talked about the tough questions her case raised for the NHS. The film we had made about Jaymee was broadcast that evening. As if to highlight the caution which had been urged by her former NHS doctors, she was in the Portland Hospital being given intravenous antibiotics to keep the graft-versus-host disease under control, but otherwise she was in good spirits.

She watched as her father appeared on the screen. 'In this case, hindsight will show that only one of us is right,' David was saying. 'If the Health Authority are right, then Jaymee would have been dead. If I'm right, then Jaymee would be alive. Well, Jaymee is alive and who's right and who's wrong doesn't really matter except to Jaymee.'

What more could a parent be expected to say? In place of the dying child he'd had to confront day after day, David Bowen could now sit and watch his daughter throw herself down the water chute in their local swimming pool, shrieking with delight. Who could possibly tell him that he'd been wrong?

But the man in charge of Cambridge Health Authority was not prepared to admit he'd been wrong either, because he did not believe he was. Stephen Thornton never wavered from his original view that what the NHS had been asked to pay for, namely a second bone marrow transplant, would not have been 'clinically effective' for Jaymee. He had never been asked to pay for donor lymphocyte infusion for the simple reason that when Jaymee began to be treated by Dr Gravett, it wasn't an option he was considering either. Over the next few days, Mr Thornton was asked time and time again whether he'd made the right decision and his answer was always yes. Furthermore, he said, he'd make the same decision again if a similar situation arose. 'I think it's important to remember that in any particular situation, you don't have the benefit of hindsight,' he said. 'You have to make a decision on the best clinical opinion that is available to you at the time, and the prevailing opinion at the time was that a second transplant would not be the right thing to do.'

Mr Thornton never denied that Jaymee had been given a chance the NHS wasn't prepared to give her and that her father had wanted her to have, but as an NHS manager he believed he'd followed the rules and made a legitimate decision for which he was prepared to be publicly accountable. 'Our whole approach is that we don't think we're doing our job unless we have a good public debate about the issues,' he said. Child B had certainly provided him with the opportunity for that, and once he realized that he had 'an issue as well as a case' on his hands, he decided that he and his colleagues would make the most of the opportunity it gave them to raise questions which were of national concern about the future shape of the NHS.

But what of the doctors who had refused to give Jaymee any more aggressive treatment? In April, shortly after she'd started being treated by Peter Gravett, I'd asked several specialists at the Royal Marsden what they would define as worthwhile 'extra time' for Jaymee, assuming that she continued to do well. Without exception they said six months of good-quality life. Now she'd had that, what would they say?

'Here we are seven months on, and after the event it's absolutely clear that what Peter Gravett did for Jaymee was worthwhile,' said Simon Meller. 'So with hindsight there is no doubt the small amount of suffering she had to go through in those first couple of months has been worthwhile in terms of the extra time she's had.' But, he added, doctors could not use the 'retrospectoscope' as the basis for clinical decision-making.

In February, when their decision was taken, a second bone marrow transplant was considered to be the only alternative treatment for Jaymee and they had ruled it out for all the reasons they had given at the time. They considered that there was no other form of treatment, experimental or otherwise, that would have been either suitable or sanctioned for use on children.

The irony was that at precisely the same time as David was being told there was nothing else that could be done for Jaymee, some adults with relapsed leukaemia of the same type as Jaymee's were being given donor lymphocyte infusion by specialists working in the same hospital.

Six months later, when Jaymee's cancer was in remission, things were beginning to change in the NHS. In the August edition of the journal *Bone Marrow Transplantation*, the doctors at the Marsden who'd treated those adult patients published their findings. There were only nine patients involved, but four had gone into complete remission. Of those, two were still alive and in remission eight and eighteen months later, respectively. It was a small study but the paper concluded: 'We plan to use this strategy as our standard approach in all relapsed acute leukaemia patients.'

Ever since the conference in Davos, there had continued to be a small but steady stream of medical papers detailing the successful results of donor lymphocyte infusion on adults, but it was only now that the official group of British children's cancer specialists agreed that it was time to set up a formal trial of the technique for children. What this meant in practice was that if David had asked the Royal Marsden for a second opinion in September rather than in February, Jaymee might well have been offered exactly the same treatment on the NHS that she'd been given by Dr Gravett in the private sector.

'The views of a number of children's transplant specialists have changed in the last six months,' said Professor Pinkerton, who, as well as having been one of Jaymee's original doctors, was on the team co-ordinating the pilot study of donor lymphocyte infusion on children. 'With hindsight, the potential complications of donor lymphocyte infusion were not so severe as was originally believed.'

'At the time Jaymee relapsed, it was too soon for anyone to say, "Give her donor lymphocytes,"' Simon Meller told me later. 'The fact that this hospital and a number of others are just starting programmes to look at donor lymphocyte infusion for acute leukaemia in children is just a sign of the times. It was about to happen when Jaymee's case came up, but it would not have been possible to do that kind of experiment within this institution in February/March 1995.'

It may indeed have been just a sign of the times, but if David had accepted what he had been told by Jaymee's doctors at the beginning of the year, she would now be dead. Instead he had chosen to gamble and so far it had paid off. Given the odds, another parent might well have decided to allow their child to die, with the reasonable certainty that the death would be painless, rather than stepping into the uncharted territory of experimental medicine. But David Bowen was not that parent.

'The gambles that I took were enormous,' he admitted, 'but they were the best, most calculated examples of thinking I've ever had to do in my life. I had to weigh up an enormous number of things before making the decision and it took me a long time to say, "Yes, this is the conclusion I've reached. It's supported by the following doctors, the following facts, the following feelings," but I think without a shadow of a doubt it was the correct one for me to make.'

During the course of the first interview with Jaymee, I'd asked her what she thought would have happened if she hadn't met Peter Gravett. 'I think I would have died by now,' she replied. 'I hope I won't get ill again because otherwise there may be a chance that I lose my life.' She said then that she'd be prepared to go through everything she'd suffered over the last seven months if it meant another chance of survival. 'If it came to having to have treatment to survive, then I would have to go with it because I would have to live.'

When Jaymee said those words, she was better than she had been for months and enjoying life to the full. The week before, Dr Gravett had taken out the Hickman line which had been in place since 13 March, another milestone for Jaymee because it marked the end of her treatment, at least for the time being. It gave her confidence too, because she knew that if Peter Gravett was prepared to remove the line through which drugs could be given instantly if there was a crisis, then he must believe she was getting better. Although she'd been allowed to go swimming with the line in place, it was much more fun without it.

But no one could point to any reliable statistics to tell them what was likely to happen next. All Peter Gravett knew was that Jaymee would have a better chance of long-term remission if the positive effect of Charlotte's cells was combined with her developing a chronic form of graft-versus-host disease where it grumbled along without causing too many problems.

Over the next few weeks, Jaymee began to have difficulty breathing and it was painful to swallow. Unfortunately for her – and unusually – the graft-versus-host disease had decided to settle in her lungs. There were times when she could barely walk up a flight of stairs because she was so short of breath. It was frightening for Jaymee and for anyone else in the family who saw what happened when she began to struggle for breath.

One day Jaymee went out with her grandfather, and from the moment they set off Ossie could see that she was having problems with her breathing. 'First I noticed that her voice was going and she was short of breath,' he remembered. 'I said, "Are you all right?" She said no, so we just walked very, very slowly. Later in the day, before we got the tube to come home, I asked her if she'd like some food and she said yes. While we were eating, I saw her swallowing in pain and I asked her if she was all right. She said, "I'm in pain."'

Ossie rang David and suggested he take her straight to Peter Gravett. They went round to his consulting rooms in Harley Street and waited while he saw another patient. After he had examined Jaymee, Peter Gravett told Ossie that Jaymee was suffering from the effects of chronic graft-versus-host disease and suggested referring her to a consultant at the renowned Brompton Hospital, for further tests on her lungs.

'Having got over the first few weeks, the graft-versus-host disease is now more of a problem for Jaymee than her leukaemia,' Dr Gravett said.

It meant she would have to remain on relatively high doses of steroids – which would help control the disease but at the same time make her more vulnerable to infection – and cyclosporin, an anti-rejection drug, which would help ensure that the reaction did not fizzle out altogether. Peter Gravett had hoped to reduce the amount of drugs Jaymee was taking; but when he'd cut down the steroids her lungs had got worse, so he could see that, for the moment at least, the risks were too great.

After Ossie and Jaymee had seen Dr Gravett, they began their journey home. They had to change trains several times, and by the time they reached Elephant and Castle Jaymee was too short of breath to walk up the stairs. 'I said, "OK, I'll carry you,"' Ossie told me. 'So there I was, lifting this big baby up all the stairs and everybody was looking at me.' By then, Jaymee's face had been all over the newspapers and television and several of the passers-by recognized her. Somehow they managed to get back to Tooting Broadway, the nearest station to Ossie and Rita's house. But Jaymee could hardly move. 'We had to walk along an alleyway about a hundred yards long to get to the car park and suddenly Jaymee just stopped. She said, "Grandad, I can't go any further."' Ossie managed to carry her to the car and she lay down in the back struggling for breath. 'It was very, very frightening,' Ossie said. In the car he gave Jaymee the inhaler he used to control his asthma and it seemed to help. But it wasn't the first time this had happened.

A few weeks before, Jaymee collapsed at a cousin's birthday party. Rita had been on her way to collect her. On the way to the house an ambulance had rushed past, but she hardly acknowledged it until she arrived at the house where the party had been and found no one there. 'I phoned my daughter and she said, "Oh Mum, Jaymee collapsed at the party and had to be taken to hospital." Then I realized that the ambulance that had screamed past me on the road had got Jaymee in it. So I got in the car thinking, Please God just let her live. I don't know how I got to the hospital. When I arrived I just ran in because I knew she mustn't be given any drugs.'

Jaymee had been given so many powerful drugs over the last five years that it was vital that no one gave her any more without knowing her medical history. The Bowen family knew only too well that the wrong combination of drugs could kill her. Luckily for Jaymee, she had been with a relative when she collapsed. In the ambulance Jaymee was given oxygen to help her breathe, nothing else. Later that evening she was well enough to go home, but after these two occasions David became even more protective of his daughter. Apart from letting her go to school, he was reluctant to allow her out of his sight for very long – just in case. David knew the function of every drug she was taking and he wanted her never to be in a situation where she might be at risk simply because the people with her were ignorant of her medical condition.

Although Jaymee's leukaemia remained in remission, her quality of life was now not as good as it had been earlier in the summer and she was dispirited by what she felt was a setback after all the positive results of the previous month. However, David was determined to keep her spirits up. Knowing she was in remission, he refused to believe that anything could now be seriously wrong. But Jaymee saw it differently.

'Well, I like to think Daddy knows what I'm feeling, but he doesn't,' she told me. 'I'll tell him I'm out of breath and he'll say, "Oh come on, you can manage that little bit extra, can't you?" And I'll say no. He'll tell me I'm fine. I say, "If I'm fine why am I struggling?" I wish he'd put himself in my shoes for just one day.'

It was difficult for them both. When David looked at Jaymee, he saw only the extraordinary improvement there had been in her health since earlier in the year. She was alive, that was all that mattered. The difficulties she was having with the graft-versus-host disease were problems which Peter Gravett could overcome with a careful adjustment of drugs. To Jaymee, though, it was just one more obstacle in the way of a normality she was desperate to regain.

'Hopefully, and I say hopefully, I will actually get a normal life after this,' she said in November, when the problems with her lungs were particularly bad.

By now there had been another change in the Bowen family too. David had decided to move away from the Cambridge area after his experience with the Health Authority and to make a new start with the children somewhere closer to London. He also wanted to be nearer to Peter Gravett if anything went wrong. He found a house for rent in a small village in Hertfordshire, and in October he and the girls moved home yet again. For the time being, Susan would remain in Cambridgeshire with Phoebe and her two sons. Over the past year she had had to get used to being without David for much of the time as most of his attention was devoted to Jaymee, and inevitably his relationship with Susan had to take second place. It meant new schools for both Jaymee and Charlotte, only a month after the start of the autumn term. Charlotte had joined Jaymee at Scaltback School in September and had been glad of her support. 'When we were both at Scaltback and no one would play with me, Jaymee came up to me and said, "I'll find someone to play with you," and I said thank you and she said, "That's OK."' Now they both had to fend for themselves and make new friends. Jaymee in particular missed her old school, where she had been accepted for who she was.

However hard she tried to be normal, the publicity surrounding her made it very difficult. As far as she was concerned, she had never wanted to be a public figure and was intensely embarrassed by all the media attention. Yet what she had said about her illness at the time the anonymity order was lifted had struck a chord which wasn't easily forgotten, and on 12 December 1995 Jaymee was one of eight children to be honoured in the annual Children of Courage Awards, presented by the Duchess of Kent in Westminster Abbey. The citation read: 'Her words of strength and hope have inspired and affected all those who have heard her story.'

Jaymee stood up in front of the assembled congregation and read a section of the Nativity. It was word-perfect and her voice was strong and clear. David stood watching her with tears in his eyes. 'I remember looking at her standing up there and thinking, That's my daughter and she's achieved so much, she's done so well. She's never, never, never, let me down, ever, not once.'

As he watched her, David also thought of the other people who had helped Jaymee get to where she was today, in particular Peter Gravett, who he thought should also have received an award for his courage in being willing to 'stick his professional neck on the line'.

Once again, Jaymee found herself the centre of attention, with newspapers and television journalists queueing up to talk to her and to ask her the question she most disliked. 'How do you feel?' they wanted to know. 'I'm fine,' she'd reply, trying hard to think of something else to say.

*

It was nearly Christmas and Jaymee was planning to make the most of it. A huge Christmas tree, beautifully decorated, surrounded by presents for Jaymee and Charlotte, stood in the dining room of their new house. Jaymee, ever meticulous, had bought most of her presents early and had already wrapped them up. Now she was busy designing and making her own Christmas cards, using wool and coloured paper. One of the cards, with a beautifully designed snowman on the front, was for Peter Gravett.

David's brother Graham was coming over from California with his children to join the family for Christmas, so there would be a large gathering, divided between Ossie and Rita's house and David's in Hertfordshire. Just before Christmas, Susan and her children moved in with David, Jaymee and Charlotte. The fridge and freezer were overflowing with food. Jaymee, bustling around like the mother hen she was when she was feeling well, just wanted everything to go smoothly. The last thing she wanted to think about was the possibility that without her father's determination the Bowens would have been facing the prospect of Christmas without her.

She'd been hoping to see Debbie before Christmas too and had bought a present for her and for James and Alexander. On the Friday before Christmas, David took the girls to spend the day at Debbie's house. Jaymee and Charlotte wished they could see more of her and hoped that once they were settled in their new home in Hertfordshire, visits would be more regular than they had been during the previous year, when so much of their time had been spent going backwards and forwards to hospital. The girls missed having a mother figure around, and as they approached adolescence they were both aware that there were things they'd find it difficult to discuss with David.

But, as he watched Jaymee sitting on the floor in their new home surrounded by wrapping paper and ribbon, all

David could think of was how different Christmas might have been had he been less belligerent. 'The best Christmas present I could have had in my entire life was my daughter and she's here. That's all that matters,' he said. 'You can't make me feel any better than this.'

15

What Price a Life?

On the rare occasions when Jaymee thinks about the future, she likes to imagine it free of hospitals and drugs, free of leukaemia, a future in which she can simply be an ordinary girl. But like anyone who has suffered from cancer, she knows there are no guarantees of survival, only the possibility that with the best possible treatment it will lie dormant for months, even years, and the tantalizing promise that the longer it remains in remission, the better the chance of it never coming back.

By the New Year, Jaymee's leukaemia had been in remission for eight months and she had confounded almost every prediction her NHS doctors had made. In January 1995 they'd told David she had only eight weeks to live, yet here she was almost exactly a year later, preparing for a new term at school. They'd said giving her more chemotherapy was pointless because it was unlikely she would go into remission, but they'd been wrong about that too. They'd said the chances of her surviving a second bone marrow transplant were so small that it wouldn't be justified. There'd been general agreement about that, but there were alternatives the NHS refused to offer, leaving her father to find another doctor who gave her exactly the same treatment that she could, at least in theory, have been given by the NHS itself.

On the face of it, 'The Story of Child B' was an extraordinary success story. But everyone who had been involved with Jaymee's treatment, including Peter Gravett, knew how differently it could have turned out.

'There were enormous risks,' said Simon Meller. 'Jaymee's freedom from leukaemia is wonderful, but no one can predict how long it's going to last. What I resent is the implication that decisions made by very experienced NHS consultants are, have been and will be wrong, and that you might be better if you get £100,000 out of your health authority and go doctor-shopping. That would be very, very dangerous.

'The public may be very much swayed by one wonderful case, but doctors are wary of anecdotes because the anecdotes people talk about are the ones that have a happy ending. It's for that reason that if you're going to start looking at a new treatment you've got to be absolutely rigorous with your method, you've got to make sure each eligible case receives the treatment, and that the reporting is complete. Otherwise you may be misled into thinking that the treatment you're investigating is much more successful than it really is.'

But what some of the adult-leukaemia specialists so disagreed with about this statement was its tacit admission that children might die unnecessarily simply because the timing of their illness happened not to coincide with the availability of a suitable NHS clinical trial. 'We are doctors, not robots,' Professor Goldman had said, with the clear implication that there was nothing wrong in demonstrating a little pioneering spirit. One year on, the medical politics surrounding Jaymee's case were as cut-throat as ever.

And what of the parents faced with the ultimatum David had been faced with a year before? All he had done was to ask questions in the hope of finding an alternative to what he was being told was an inevitable death. A year later, not only was Jaymee still alive, but the evidence emerging from the NHS about the use of donor lymphocyte infusion in acute leukaemia patients continued to be encouraging, particularly for those patients given the treatment after chemotherapy had succeeded in getting their leukaemia into remission. Jaymee had been in that category, although no one had known for sure until after she'd been given the first dose of Charlotte's cells that the intensive dose of chemotherapy she'd been given under sedation had worked.

'This wasn't a clear-cut case,' David said. 'It was a case in which there were differing opinions, differing eminent opinions – that was the problem. Who is supposed to reconcile those different views?'

The prospect of Jaymee's case eroding the trust between parents and doctors was what had most concerned the NHS children's cancer specialists. Apart from the challenge to their professional authority, more important was the risk that some parents would feel that unless they followed the same path as David Bowen, they would be failing their children.

In Jaymee's case, it had fallen to a manager, not a doctor, to make the final decision – a job David said he could never do because he would always have to give someone the benefit of the doubt. 'I know there's always a chance and I couldn't sign off someone's life knowing there was a chance. I couldn't do that to another human being.' At the back of his mind is the question David hopes never to have to confront. If Jaymee's leukaemia relapsed again, would he still believe that simply knowing there was 'a chance' was enough to justify subjecting her to yet more aggressive treatment?

'We'll go through exactly what we did this time,' was David's prompt reply.

But what of Jaymee herself? So much of the truth about her illness was kept from her at such a crucial time that it is difficult for her to be precise about how she feels, because many of the feelings she had at the time were based on what she later discovered was fiction rather than fact. If her cancer came back again, knowing what she does now, how much would she be prepared to suffer in order to have another chance of life? When we first talked about this in the interview she recorded for *Panorama*, Jaymee seemed to be in no doubt that she would go through it all again. But when we talked about it one afternoon almost three months later, when the problems with her breathing were particularly bad, she seemed much less certain.

'I'd give up straight away. I tell you now I don't feel like doing it again,' she said. 'I've had four lots of treatment already and there just comes a time when you can't go on with it. You just give up. Four times is too much.' I asked her if she was really serious. It seemed such a volte-face. 'I can't face it any more, really,' she said. Even if it meant dying? 'Yes,' she replied. That day she said she had prepared herself for death. 'There's nothing to be scared of,' she said, adding, 'And hopefully it won't be painful.'

Given what she has been through, it is inevitable that Jaymee should have moments of doubt. But David says he would need to know that her reluctance to have more treatment was genuine and not simply because of how she happened to be feeling at the time. Just like his daughter, it takes a great deal to make David Bowen give up. 'I'd have to be very sure that she was making the decision for the right reasons,' David said. 'I'd rationalize with her. I know her well enough to know that she has down days, when she's just fed up with the whole world. I'd have to be sure that it was really her wish; but knowing her as I do, I do not believe that she is capable of saying that under any circumstances.'

But perhaps he hadn't bargained for Jaymee's determination, that sheer obstinacy she's so obviously inherited from him. 'If he wants to respect my wishes, then he'll accept it. If he's already lined me up with more treatment, then if I feel it's not worth it, I wouldn't do it,' Jaymee said. It was hard to believe that this was the same Jaymee Bowen who had been so dismissive of children who might refuse treatment. Would she really be prepared to say no? 'It would be very difficult for me to refuse. If he arranges it behind my back, I would obviously be very upset. I'd feel really bad, but I want to be strong enough to refuse. Everyone has to die some day. Some earlier than others.'

That same day, I'd been talking to Charlotte. She said she was convinced that Jaymee had been thinking about the possibility that she might die. 'She's prepared herself well for everything. She's been packing everything, you can tell. She's packed everything away where it should be so that if she dies no one can touch it, and people can come by and say that room was where Jaymee last lived. She does things for the strangest reasons – she can't really explain what she's doing.'

Both David's parents are certain that if Jaymee relapsed, he would do everything he could to have her treated. 'The only way he will give up is if every person he speaks to, every doctor, says, "No chance, I won't do it." That's the only way,' Ossie told me.

It is the scenario everyone hopes the Bowen family will not have to face. Yet with cancer as complex as Jaymee's, time and success are measured differently. If she remains in remission for a year, it will be two months longer than the remission she achieved after her bone marrow transplant; and if she is still in remission after eighteen months, Peter Gravett says he will take Jaymee off all the drugs and hope for the best. What that will be, no one can predict, since Jaymee has already defied the medical odds. But her chance of long-term remission from cancer is now significantly higher than it was when she began to be treated by Peter Gravett.

'It's like the sword of Damocles,' David said. 'The only thing is you appreciate that, as time goes by, the cancer is less likely to come back.' But by the middle of January, it was becoming clear that the price being paid to keep Jaymee's leukaemia in remission was getting higher as the months went by.

On 17 January 1996, exactly one year after David received the letter from Addenbrooke's Hospital telling him that there were some 'abnormalities' in Jaymee's blood, the Bowens celebrated Charlotte's tenth birthday. As a special treat, David had given her several hundred pounds to choose presents for herself in Hamley's toy-shop in Regent Street. In the afternoon, David, Jaymee, Charlotte and Susan had tea at the Ritz, where Charlotte sat surrounded by all her purchases. She was in her element, but like so many other years it was Jaymee's health which was uppermost in everyone's mind. The birthday party planned for Charlotte the following weekend had been postponed because Jaymee was to spend two days in hospital being given a large dose of steroids to try and control the graft-versus-host disease which by now was seriously affecting her quality of life. Her lungs were getting worse and she was hardly eating. As a result she seemed permanently tired and was unable to run or swim or join in any sport at school. In spite of these problems, her leukaemia remained in remission. It meant Peter Gravett was faced with trying to maintain an increasingly delicate balance.

'I'm caught between the devil and the deep blue sea,' he said. 'If I give her more steroids, they will control her breathing problems but it's not good for her leukaemia because they'll suppress her immune system and switch off the graft-versus-host disease.'

At this stage it was impossible to know whether the damage to Jaymee's lungs would be permanent or vanish once the graft-versus-host disease fizzled out, but it was obvious that something had to be done because the regular tests she was having at the Brompton Hospital showed her 'lung function' was deteriorating.

Assuming the steroids succeeded in controlling the graft-versus-host disease, the next problem was what should be done when it did disappear, something which usually happens roughly one year after the start of treatment. That date was fast approaching, and Peter Gravett believed it would be too risky to give Jaymee any more of Charlotte's cells even though he still had several doses stored in the freezer. The danger of sparking off a reaction which would result in permanent damage to her lungs was just too great.

Without more of Charlotte's cells, Jaymee may have to take her chances without further treatment in the hope that she remains in remission. If after eighteen months the cancer has still not returned, Peter Gravett says that current evidence on the use of donor lymphocyte infusion suggests there will be a 70 per cent chance that Jaymee's leukaemia will never come back.

As for Jaymee herself, she prefers not to look too far ahead. The last six years have taught her never to raise her hopes too high. As I write this, exactly a year after Jaymee's original doctors decided there was nothing more they could do, it would be both unjustified and cruel to say that the enormous efforts which have been made on her behalf have not been worth it. She is alive and her cancer is still in remission – she could so easily have been dead. In simple terms, perhaps that is the only bottom line worth measuring, but Jaymee's story is not a simple one.

'Never give up unless you are on the last little drop of life. Never give up.' Jaymee's words are not easily forgotten and she remains an indomitable fighter. But if the worst should happen, she has prepared herself for that too. 'I don't want to die,' she said. 'But if I do and there is an afterlife, I want to come back as a butterfly.' Fragile, but free.